STRANGE SEA STORIES

ALSO BY MARIE A. LAWSON

THE SEA IS BLUE

STRANGE SEA STORIES

Legends, Lore, and Superstitions of the Mysterious Waters, by

MARIE A. LAWSON

1955

THE VIKING PRESS, NEW YORK

First published by The Viking Press in December 1955
Published on the same day in the Dominion of Canada
by The Macmillan Company of Canada Limited

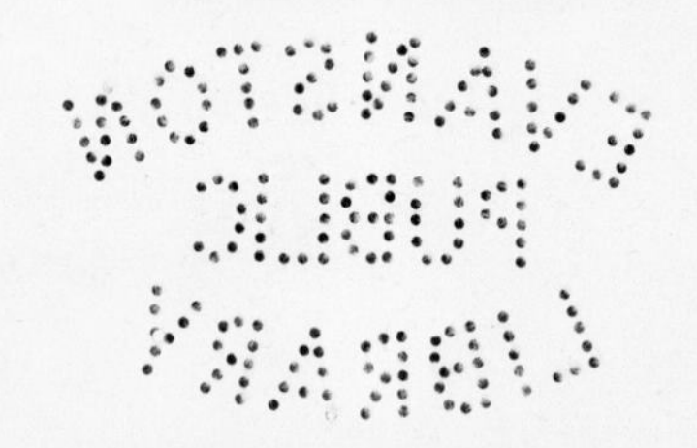

PRINTED IN THE U. S. A. BY THE VAIL-BALLOU PRESS INC.

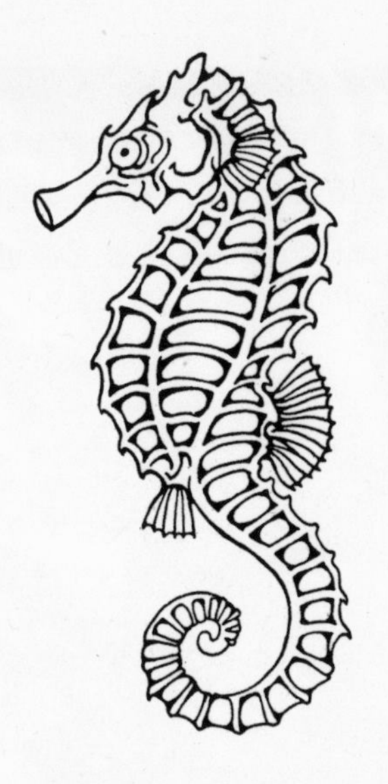

TO MY AUNT JUNE

We share a common heritage:
A deep love of the sea.

ATLANTIS

What poets sang in Atlantis? Who can tell
The epics of Atlantis or their names?
The sea has its own murmurs, and sounds not
The secrets of its silences beneath,
And knows not any cadences enfolded
When the last bubbles of Atlantis broke
Among the quieting of its heaving floor.

—Gordon Bottomley

CONTENTS

"Atlantis" by Gordon Bottomley 6
Prologue 9
The Seven Seas 11
"The Child and the Mariner" by William H. Davies 14

PHANTOM SHIPS
The Flying Dutchman 17
Captain Fokke of Holland 24
A Game of Dice 34

HORSES OF THE SEA
The Wonderful Horse 44
"The Moon-Child" by Fiona Macleod 54

THE SEALS
The Wife of Bjorn Bryn 57
Kirsten McVurich 69

STRANGE FOLK OF THE SEA
Martin Grogan and the Merrow 83
The Coral Comb 94

THE NECK
The Neck 102

THE FAR HORIZON
The Maker of Maps 115

FIGUREHEADS
The Figurehead 132

SUPERSTITIONS

The Little Book 143

WIND AND TEMPEST

Sixpence for a Breeze 156

A Pound of Tobacco 162

UNLUCKY PASSENGERS

The Voyage of *The Lass of Glasgow* 165

TERRORS OF THE SEA

The Sea Serpent 180

PROLOGUE

TODAY the route of the ocean voyager is written on a chart; he has the benefit of accurate instruments, the gleam of lighthouses as guidance, the ringing bells of buoys as warning of jagged rock or shallow water. Science has measured the surfaces of the seas in nautical miles, the depths in fathoms.

Despite all this, the sea roads are still only upon the charts, not upon the sea herself. The vessels of all nations have voyaged upon her; mighty battles have raged and reeling ships gone down with their courageous crews, their passing marked, for a brief moment, by a ripple of cleft waves, a drift of white foam.

That is all.

The sea the modern mariner looks upon is the same sea the first sailor gazed upon with awe and allurement. Her beauty is ageless and unscarred. Her enchantment is written anew with each generation of men who choose the hard sea life; her appalling power still speaks when the huge modern ships of steel and steam go down before her unconquerable anger.

Ever-increasing knowledge, slowly and dangerously acquired throughout the ages, has cleared up some of the mystery which in older days hung over the sea like a mist. But secret and savage she still remains; and perhaps because of this strange tales have lingered long among the folk who live close to the waters and among the men who sail upon them.

THE SEVEN SEAS

We were the first that ever burst,
Into that silent sea.
—Samuel Taylor Coleridge, "The Ancient Mariner"

MANY bodies of water are called seas, but the term "the Seven Seas" refers to the largest of all, the oceans: the Arctic and Antarctic, the North and South Atlantic, the North and South Pacific, and the Indian.

The Indian Ocean takes its name from the country along its northern shore, India, whose name, in turn, came from "Sindhu," meaning river. India was called in olden days "the land beyond the river."

The Indian Ocean is a dangerous body of water, full of treacherous rocks and hidden reefs of coral, and given to sudden and violent storms. The Phoenicians are believed occasionally to have ventured into it, but it was little known until the ninth century A.D., when it became a highway for the traders of Arabia. Not until late in the fifteenth century did it become known to the seamen of Europe.

In the middle ages the Atlantic Ocean was called "the Sea of Darkness." Men knew its eastern shores; they had managed to get as far as the Azores and Canary Islands. Beyond this point truly lay darkness, a darkness bred of ignorance and of fear. This ocean remained virtually unknown until Christopher Columbus dared cross its vast reaches and found a new world.

The origin of its name is still uncertain—possibly it was taken from the towering Atlas mountains, which look down upon its stormy waters, or from the fabled lost land of Atlantis, believed to lie somewhere in its depths.

The Pacific, the largest ocean of all, was first seen by European eyes in 1513, when a Spanish explorer, Vasco Nuñez de Balboa, lured by red men's tales of immense waters to the west, beat his way through the dense and steaming jungles of Panama to behold, at last, that seemingly endless calm blue sea. He called it simply, "Mar del Sud"—the Sea of the South. A later explorer, Ferdinand Magellan of Portugal, amazed at the serenity of its immense surface, gave it its permanent name, Pacific, meaning peaceful.

The Arctic Ocean, which surrounds the ice-choked North Pole, has not yet been fully explored. The first dim record of its discovery is that of a courageous sailor of Norway, Othere, who told Alfred the Great, first king of England, of his adventure into the forbidding White Sea. Othere and his astounded crew were perhaps the first to behold the dark bulks of the terrifying killer whales or the snowy polar bears, moving, like phantoms, across the ice floes.

The name Arctic comes from *arktos,* the Greek word for "bear," and was given to the region around the North Pole because over it shine the brilliant constellations of

the Great Bear and the Little Bear—better known to us today as the Big and Little Dippers.

The Antarctic, from the same word plus "ant" meaning "opposite," is the name of the ocean, and the region, opposite the region of the Bears—around the South Pole. It was close on nine centuries after Othere had dared the ice of the Arctic that the Antarctic, last-known of the great oceans, was charted by Captain James Cook, explorer for England, in the year 1773. Captain Cook and his men saw neither killer whales nor ghostly bears, but they were assuredly the first to behold the most remarkable birds in all creation—the penguins.

THE CHILD AND THE MARINER

This sailor knows of wondrous lands afar,
More rich than Spain, when the Phoenicians shipped
Silver for common ballast, and they saw
Horses at silver mangers eating grain;
This man has seen the wind blow up a mermaid's hair
Which, like a golden serpent, reared and stretched
To feel the air away beyond her head. . . .
He many a tale of wonder told: of where,
At Argostoli, Cephalonia's sea
Ran over the earth's lip in heavy floods;
And then again of how the strange Chinese
Conversed much as our homely blackbirds sing.
He told us how he sailed in one old ship
Near that volcano Martinique, whose power
Shook like dry leaves the whole Caribbean seas;
And made the sun set in a sea of fire
Which only half was his; and dust was thick
On deck, and stones were pelted at the mast. . . .
He told how isles sprang up and sank again,
Between short voyages, to his amaze:
How they did come and go, and cheated charts:
Told how a crew was cursed when one man killed
A bird that perched upon a moving barque;
And how the sea's sharp needles, firm and strong,
Ripped open the bellies of big, iron ships:
Of mighty icebergs in the Northern seas,

That haunt the far horizon like white ghosts.
He told of waves which lift a ship so high
That birds could pass from starboard unto port
Under her dripping keel.

Oh, it was sweet
To hear that seaman tell such wondrous tales. . . .

—William H. Davies

PHANTOM SHIPS

THE BELIEF in phantom ships has persisted throughout the ages, and the sight of one has often been thought to be a sure sign of storm or dire disaster. Many of these ships have been seen off shores all over the world, and various tales have been told—of ships filled with people, ablaze with lights, merry with music and song; and of ships apparently signaling for a pilot, then suddenly disappearing.

Most of these vessels are nameless, and the accounts as mere mist upon the sea. But there are a few more definite.

There is the swift dark ship seen for centuries in the tempestuous North Sea; and off the dangerous waters of the Cape of Good Hope the ship of Captain Fokke of Holland, who was famed for his mysteriously short voyages.

Best known of all, of course, is the *Flying Dutchman,* seen around that same stormy Cape. Why this luckless ship, weatherbeaten and weary, cruises on and on has been a matter of much argument. Some say a murder was committed on board and the sailors dared not land; others that a plague broke out and no port would give them harborage; yet another story is that the captain, Cornelius Vanderdecken, struggling against the raging winds and waves of the cape, swore with appalling oaths that he would round that cape if it took him until Judgment Day. So, say the pious, in punishment for his profanity he must keep trying until that momentous day arrives.

THE FLYING DUTCHMAN

NO SAILOR likes to see the *Flying Dutchman,* for it is likely to be a sign of stormy seas and ill luck to come. But her master, Captain Cornelius Vanderdecken, is a friendly soul—or seems so. Unlike the captains of other phantom ships, he has more than once hailed passing ships, and cordially invited the officers to come aboard for a tot of spirits and a chat. Now no man has ever quite dared to do that, lest he be taken away. But some have invited Captain Vanderdecken to visit them, for though they fear bad luck, they fear it might be worse if they did not. Many such visits have been reported, and no harm done.

But there was one ship; it is well to be silent on her name and her post, lest she still be sailing—and her experience was strange indeed.

It was a day of blue skies and sunshine and towering banks of clouds. Suddenly the clouds became great sails, and, clearly, the astonished crew saw the *Flying Dutchman* before them, with her high carved poop and her gay flag, and heard a bluff voice accepting their captain's invitation. They saw the boat lowered, and soon Captain Vanderdecken clambered over the side of their ship. He was finely dressed, with a deal of gold braid and many brass buttons, which winked like jewels in the sun. Most genial and jolly he seemed, making inquiries about their voyage, as any well-bred captain would; praising the flavor of their rum, the freshness of their biscuits. He requested that they mail some letters for him at their next port of landing. The letters were addressed in a fine, firm hand and sealed neatly with black wax.

But before the captain's boat reached the *Flying Dutchman* again the piled white clouds had turned gray, then black, shutting out the sun. A fog had risen on the water, and the wind was whining in the rigging. The men could not see the *Flying Dutchman* at all.

All of them were a trifle shaken by the visit, and a frightened murmur arose among the crew. None of them had heard the shout of an order or the flap of a sail or the rasp of a rope or the rattle of an anchor chain—and that is a loud noise, even in a storm.

The strange ship was just gone.

The chief mate was a stolid, sensible man and tried to calm his men. Mercifully there was much to do; they had to get busy, for the storm was increasing in violence. Zigzag lightning gashed the black skies, and the thunder was like cannon in a battle. Above the shouts, the stamp of flying feet, the moan of the wind, the mate heard the tearing of a sail, then another, the flapping of broken ropes. He wondered where the captain was, for he sorely needed him at the wheel.

Then the cabin boy came to say the captain seemed most woefully weary and would like a short rest before taking over. A sudden misgiving struck even the mate's stout heart. "Is your master ill?"

"No, sir," piped the shrill small voice at his elbow, "not at all. The cook is in there now, taking orders for supper. And Captain has ordered both salt beef and pork and some of the fresh fish we caught yesterday night and a bite of pudding, and a noggin of rum for all hands, it being an odd afternoon, and a bad night to come."

The mate's hands were almost numb upon the wheel when the captain came, reaching out strong hands for the plunging wheel. Just then lightning lighted the sky, and the mate saw that the captain's face was grim and gray under its heavy tan.

"It was a kind thought and a wise one," said the mate, "to order so good a supper. The crew will work better on full stomachs, and it will hearten them as well."

But the captain's face grew more ashen and more grim. "A good thought," he answered, "and only a thought it remains. The cook has just reported that we have no beef, no pork, no fish. Not a potato or a dried apple. Every scrap of our food has turned to beans. And every drop of our rum has become sour vinegar in the casks!"

About midnight the skies cleared, a pale, watery moon appeared, and the wind died.

"We are a long way from any port," said the captain wearily.

"Take a rest, sir," said the mate. "I will take over again."

So the captain went below, and more than one sailor noted that he walked like an old man.

It was in the gray dawn that the weary mate heard the sound of running feet, light feet, heavy feet—the cabin boy, the big cook, officers, sailors. There was a babble of confused voices.

"The captain, sir." "Come at once!" "I'll take the wheel." "It's that accursed Dutchman, Vanderdecken, brought this upon us!" "How far are we from land?"

The mate scarcely remembered getting below.

The captain was not gray now, but the terrible white of a wax candle. He was struggling with two stalwart seamen. There were fragments of broken and chewed rope upon the cabin floor, and a litter of letters—opened

letters—their envelopes bearing bits of black sealing wax.

Again the voices rose.

"We tried to tie him, sir." "He wanted to jump overboard!" "He is, I fear, sir, quite mad."

There was no question of that, and the mate suddenly remembered some old tales of the peril of reading letters from the *Flying Dutchman*. Why, oh why, had the good captain done that? Perhaps hoping to solve forever the mystery of that phantom ship?

"Pick up those letters," he ordered the shaking cabin boy, "and give them to me. Don't miss a scrap of paper, not even a bit of broken sealing wax."

The cabin boy obeyed. The mate put them in the pockets of his storm coat. His face was nearly as drawn as the captain's.

By nightfall they had to put the captain in chains, for so strong he was, and so frantic, he could break a stout rope or chew it through in an hour. And no three men could hold him.

The night was clear, with a gentle breeze, and the tired men could relax a bit. So the officers, the sailors from the forecastle, even the young cabin boy, gathered together in unwonted democracy and comradeship. They whispered together and all agreed. Something must be done.

The mate, on whom they depended to steer the ship home, had those fateful letters. Might not curiosity overcome him, as it had their honest captain? They decided to elect a delegation to call upon the mate, selecting nine as a lucky number. And the nine, in turn, chose the burly bosun as spokesman.

Gravely and quietly they went forward to where the mate was steering. He turned his head but there was no surprise on his face. He signaled to the second mate to take the wheel, and faced them.

"Mister mate," said the bosun, "you are now master of this ship, and we most unworthy to interfere or ask questions, but—but you have those evil letters. Might we not throw them overboard, that we might rest the better?"

"Throw them overboard?" said he. "For some other luckless vessel to pick up? Never! But you may rest easy. I burned them in the galley stove at once. The cook will bear witness."

For the first time in many long hours he was smiling.

"As for our captain, he is much better. Tell them." And he nodded to the big cook.

"The captain was able to eat a small measure of beans for his supper," said the grinning cook. "He asked for them himself, and very clear he spoke, and quiet, like his old self. And he left not one bean upon his plate—not one."

And so the ship came home to her port, but little could ever be got from the crew about that voyage. Only the young cabin boy talked, this being his first venture on the sea.

That is how it became known why none of the crew of that ship would ever again eat beans.

CAPTAIN FOKKE OF HOLLAND

LONG years ago there was a seaport in Holland, and so many were the ships that there were times when the multitude of masts made a veritable forest of the harbor. A most prosperous town it was, for those who did not sail ships often had a share in them. So the houses were all well built and furnished with furniture stoutly made.

But there was one house that stood out above all the others—the house of Captain Bernard Fokke. It was, to begin with, larger, more finely built, more handsomely furnished.

Not for the captain the usual stair rails of good oak, but rails of gleaming ruddy mahogany; not for him the sturdy oaken chests, but chests of dark teak, polished until they looked like black satin, and richly carved with many figures—of dragons and tiger cats and long-tailed birds and strange leafage. And in his garden grew trees and flowers never seen before in that part of the world.

As for his wife, she had many dresses in beautiful patterns and colors, and fans of thin, fragrant sandal-wood, and perfumes of haunting sweetness.

"And him, after all, merely a sailor!" said the burgo-master's wife with an envious sniff. "With a house finer than that of the chief banker and the richest merchant—even than that of the burgomaster himself."

"I'd hardly call Captain Fokke 'merely a sailor,' my love," said the good-natured burgomaster. "He's a great captain and a good trader, and he has the finest ship that ever anchored in our harbor."

"Vrouw Fokke," broke in his wife, "has finer dresses than I ever expect to see, and I hear on his last voyage he brought home teacups so thin the light shines through them and a shawl so fine you could run it through a ring."

"Mayhap," said the burgomaster, "he put in at China

or India." And before his wife could draw breath again he went on, "You can never say Captain Fokke is not a generous man. Doesn't every child in the town run to meet his ship, for all the fruits and sweetmeats he gives them? And that coffee he brought to us is nectar for the gods! And did he not offer you a chest of rare spices and one of the gay little birds from Java?"

"He did," answered the burgomaster's wife reluctantly, "but I didn't want the bird. It does not sing; it is merely bright-colored, like Vrouw Fokke herself. And I'm not sure I like all those strange, foreign spices in good, honest dough. And as for that great bird with a tail it can scarce carry and a voice to wake the dead in their graves, and that dreadful little beast who looks like an old, old man; and that dark bird that talks—and often as not it's talk picked up from the swearing, sinful sailors—I'd give none of them house room!"

The burgomaster knew there was no use to argue with the good wife, so out he went to seek the possible quiet of his snug office. As for himself, well, he had greatly enjoyed the spicy little cakes at Vrouw Fokke's; he had thought the peacock a miracle of beauty; had been fascinated by the small monkey; and as for that miraculous mynah bird with its mischievous tongue, he could listen to it the day long. And he and Bernard Fokke—why, they had learned their first lessons together!

As he was nearing his office he was rousing from this dream of old days by seeing his young clerk, hastening at top speed to meet him. "Captain Fokke's ship has been sighted," he gasped, "still a way off. The sexton saw it from the high church tower—"

"But," said the burgomaster, amazed, "he could not have gone all the way to Java and back. He only sailed—perhaps I am mistaken in the date?" He bustled into his office and consulted a ledger. "No, I am right in my memory of the date. He must have been disabled, and turned back."

The young clerk turned from the window, and his face was grave. "The voyages grow shorter and shorter, sir, and—perhaps I should not be so bold as to tell you, but I think you should know—there are whispers in the town. They are rather odd whispers."

The burgomaster rose heavily to go to the windows. "Thank you, Pieter," he said, "for telling me. Yes, I should know."

Now they saw the children running to the quays, saw the big ship warping in, saw the great sails coming down like folded wings, heard the harsh rattle of the anchor chains. By that time there was a crowd gathering, and even before they reached the quay the hatches were being opened. From them spread the mingled aroma long associated with Captain Fokke's ship. Such a cargo could only have come from those far-off fruitful lands—from Java—and—

The burgomaster felt strangely shaken. The shortness of this voyage was impossible, perplexing.

"Perhaps," whispered young Pieter, "Captain Fokke has found a shorter route."

But the captain had not. He wrung the burgomaster's hand with warmth. "A new route?" said he. "Not at all—just the best of luck, remarkable luck, my friend. Winds favorable and fine going and coming and the wicked old Cape quiet for once. I've brought you some coffee—a new blend. Why, it will make the other taste like bilge water in comparison."

Captain Fokke's next voyage was even shorter—and the next. The whispers grew louder in the town. Old mariners consulted their yellowed charts, measured distances, calculated time—and shook their heads. They questioned the sailors in the taverns, but from Captain Fokke's men they got nothing at all.

"Ah," said Fokke's burly bosun, "in your sailing days you never had such a ship as this. She takes the waves like a dolphin, and her sails are like a thousand flying seabirds."

And the young sailors would only laugh and tease the old mariners.

"This is a new age," one would say. "We no longer have to sail those old round tubs in which you could scarce tell the bow from the stern."

Then another would break in. "And we no longer have those clumsy, weighty sails—ours go up lightly, swiftly, in time to catch the good winds while they are blowing."

And yet another would chime in. "Nor are we held back from sailing by ancient tales—like the one of a

frisky cat who has 'a gale in her tail'—or by a dog howling on the dock."

But the old seamen continued to shake their heads, and the echoes of their muttering drifted into the homes, and housewives whispered together over their coffee and cakes. Even the youngest children caught fragments of the whispers, and, awestruck, repeated them among themselves.

There was something very, very strange about these brief voyages—something uncanny. Vrouw Fokke had many a cold refusal to her invitations; neighbors complained about the screams of the peacock; there were hostile eyes when she entered the church; and many children wept because they were forbidden to meet Captain Fokke's ship when it came in. The whispers were louder—open talk now. There was mention of souls—of bargains with the Powers of Darkness.

The pastor even spoke from the pulpit. "I dislike," said he, "to speak ill of a fellow citizen—or of any man. But it has been brought to my attention that certain recent voyages have been—well—unbelievably brief." He consulted some papers and coughed. "It has been proved to me, by some of our revered and experienced mariners, that certain distances take a certain amount of time. It has been denied that a shorter route has been found between this port and those faraway lands Holland is so fortunate to own.

"These recent voyages have been too short, far too short, without—er—let us say, supernatural assistance. Nor," he went on, warming to his subject, "is it likely that even our Merciful Father in Heaven could prevent every tempestuous wave or buffeting gale. He has not so favored other worthy seamen in the past; these perils are part of the sea life which many of our men have faced. There can be—there can be—I regret to say—but one alternative—"

His voice was suddenly drowned by a terrific, discordant clamor from the bells in the church tower. For a moment the congregation sat stone-still and staring. The solemn little choirboys all sat in their accustomed places; the bell-ringers sat, sedate, in the back pew.

The bells grew louder. The sexton and the bell-ringers hastened out. The burgomaster hurried to assist Vrouw Fokke, who was near fainting. A few faithful friends went with him.

Within the hour the town hummed like a beehive.

It had been Captain Fokke's monkey who had set the church bells ringing, making such a din that the pastor could not finish his sermon. That evil little monkey had known what the pastor was going to say and tried to stop him. But the townspeople knew without the telling. Unquestionably Captain Fokke had made a bargain for those swift voyages—he had bartered his immortal soul to the Devil!

Eagerly the whole town awaited the coming of the Captain's ship. Even for a normal voyage she was a bit overdue. But there was no word. Each incoming vessel was questioned. No one had sighted Captain Fokke.

At the end of a year Vrouw Fokke put away her own beautiful clothes and those of the children, and one and all they appeared in somber black. There was much comment on this, and some commendation as well. Some of the old friends drifted back. The mischievous monkey and the handsome peacock died, and the mynah bird disappeared. The Fokke sons grew up and went forth as sailors.

Now and again, but rarely, some incoming ship reported that they had seen the ship of Captain Fokke. But the details were vague.

Yes, it had been at the Cape of Good Hope. They all admitted there had been fogs, but one man had clearly seen the old flag, tattered and faded, but still recognizable. Some said one thing, some another. But all agreed that they had seen three men aboard, the captain and two others—old men, with long white beards; and, also, that the ship had never answered a friendly hail—it just disappeared in the mist and fog.

"Stuff and nonsense," said most of the townfolk. "That ship has gone long ago to the bottom of the sea. These men saw but a mass of piled clouds. Those so-called ghosts with their long white beards were mere bits of drifting fog. And the flag—well—the setting sun trying to break through the clouds—no more."

That, in general, was the opinion of all, save one old man who had spent threescore years upon the sea. "Talk on, young men," said he. "Unless the sea has changed, you may still see strange sights upon her, and hear strange sounds. It has been that way since time began. I figure it will be that way always."

Then one of Captain Fokke's sons came home, and straight to the burgomaster he went. "You have ever been a good friend," he said. "I wish to tell you something. Perhaps it should go no further, sir."

"I have known you since you could barely walk," said the burgomaster. "And I was fond indeed of your father. I have kept many secrets in my time; I can keep another."

"Thank you, sir," said young Bernard Fokke. He went on with an effort. "Sir—I have seen the old ship—and my father and his mate and the faithful bosun. They were old, old men."

"And why not?" said the burgomaster sadly. "I too am an old man. The years fly swiftly as one grows older. But—but are you quite sure, my son?"

"I would know my own father, sir, beard or not, age or not. And there was another thing—the mynah bird was on my father's shoulder. And from that silent ship it was the bird alone that answered our hail. He—he wished us a good voyage home."

A GAME OF DICE

BARON FALKENBERG was a high-tempered man and one whose touchiness about his honor was a byword in the land. Many a duel he fought, and he usually won, for he was an expert swordsman and as quick on his feet as a cat. Perfectly honorable duels they had all been, with seconds and witnesses, and, in the baron's eyes, all justifiable. He held his head high. Men admired him for his great skill, and women looked after his straight, handsomely dressed figure with admiration. Even a slight gash on his face, acquired when he had met an adversary almost as skilled as he himself, they deemed more interesting than repellent.

The baron had a stout castle, fine horses, loyal friends, and faithful retainers. All in all, he was a happy man—until— Well, the whole of this story will never be known, for the baron would not talk, the dead man could not, and the priest's profession forbids the telling of tales.

There was a duel, but there were no witnesses to the quarrel, whatever it was, or to the sudden and violent swordplay. A flaring of tempers, no doubt, a swift challenge, a too-deep sword thrust. When the baron rushed to his fallen foe, he was horrorstruck to find him dying, and, as he strove to lift him, the man reached up and left a bloody hand print on the baron's cheek.

Strangely, that hand print would not come off, not with soap or water or unguents. The baron sent for his physician, who, after many experiments, gave up in despair. Then, as the church bells were tolling for the man he had killed, the baron sent for the priest.

The priest was severe. "Many and many a time, my wayward son," he said gravely, "I have warned you against your fiery temper and your touchiness. You have many a time proved your valor and your honor in battle —you have no need to prove it in the useless and vicious practice of dueling. Now the mark of Cain is truly upon you—that Cain, first son of Adam, who slew his own young brother. I can say prayers for you, and I will, but—"

The gloomy tolling of the church bells kept on and on, and the priest flapped away in his long black cassock, and the baron sat, brooding, until his faithful servingman brought his supper.

"Milord," he said, "kindly do not think me too presuming, but—but—you have been a good master; your interest is my interest—"

The baron was grateful for the halting little speech. "Yes?" he said.

The servingman, encouraged, went on eagerly. "There is, milord, not too far from here a man famed for healing; I know you have had your own physician and the good priest, but sometimes these wise men—I will not say they know better things, but different things. I had a nephew so cross-eyed he could only look down his own nose, and this man made the boy's eyes so straight he is now the best archer in his village. And more than one hapless maid with drab hair and a pallid face has he transformed into a fair young woman with shining hair and glowing cheeks. I could send—no, no gossipy young grooms, but your own coachman, who is a trusty and loyal man—"

The baron rose and looked into a mirror; the hand print seemed more vivid than before. "Send," he said briefly. "And thank you, Johann."

So the wise man came, and tirelessly, for days and nights, he made soaps and salves and lotions, some of which were as fragrant as a garden in full summer and others so sour and bitter they were all but unendurable to smell. But the terrible telltale mark remained.

"I can do nothing," said the wise man, at the week's ending. "No—I wish no money—I have failed. But I would like to give you a bit of advice. Go to a far land where no man knows you. And go by sea, for news travels faster and farther upon the land than upon the water. So far no one here knows you killed that man—but—with that mark upon your face—" He hesitated. "Yes, in a new country you might say that it was a birthmark, though I have never seen one like it. But I happen to know that, as well as being a soldier and a swordsman, you have also been a great hunter of wild beasts. I suggest that you say that you were clawed by a savage bear,

for the claws of a bear are set much as the nails are set on the hand of a man."

Along the roads rolled the baron's fine coach, with the trusty coachman, the baron, and the faithful Johann. With each hour and every mile they could feel they were coming closer to the sea. At first there was merely a freshness in the air, then a faint whiff of marshes, then the real sea wind, strong and sharp with salt.

At a nod from the baron, Johann went into the most promising-looking of the inns and asked for accommodations. The landlord, with curious eyes, watched the tall figure of the baron, his coat collar turned up to his ears, mounting the broad stairs. Then he turned back to answer Johann's questions.

Certainly the gentleman could have his meals served in his rooms. Yes, there were a number of ships in the harbor, bound for various far ports—even now, the shipping master was making out the lists; shortly he, the landlord, would have a copy for his customers.

Sadly Johann went up to the baron's quarters. He found him sorting many papers on a table. "I will need no sailing list, Johann. There would be too many questions. I must go aboard as a stowaway, perhaps work my passage."

He rose and pointed out the window. "I have picked out my ship. See—the black one yonder; she looks fast. One last request. I am putting all these papers in one envelope; deliver them to my man-at-law, Herr Hoffritz. Merely say I have gone on a long journey. You and all my people are provided for, for all time. And"—he handed Johann a bag of coins—"pay my bills here. No, my friend, I doubt if I shall come back. Good-by."

On the stroke of midnight, when the folk of the inn were all asleep, the baron crept out and down the deserted streets to the black ship. The ship seemed to be sleeping too. He saw no one, not even a lone watchman. Cautiously he went aboard; there were a number of empty cabins, and in one he fell asleep, exhausted.

In the gray daybreak he awoke, heard the sails going up, the rattle of anchor chains, the gurgle of water against the hull as the ship got under way. But it was still an oddly silent ship. He had heard no orders of command, no shouting of sailors; and he had heard but one man walking—a strange walk, like that of a man with a wooden leg. So weary he was that he kept falling asleep, despite his fear of being found.

And then he knew that someone had found him. Three times that day he was awakened by a slight noise, to find meals beside him—breakfast, luncheon, dinner. Most delectable meals they were—many foods he had never tasted, savory with sauces and spices he did not know. But he saw no one.

After dinner that evening a voice spoke at his cabin door. "The captain is at the wheel, sir; he requests that you come up to him."

There was a tall figure at the wheel, wrapped in a long cloak, with a huge hat pulled well down.

Now the baron was in trouble indeed; he would have much to explain. And well he knew that these seafaring men asked straight questions and expected straight answers.

But, without turning, the tall man spoke before the baron could open his mouth. "I know all about you, Baron Falkenberg; you need tell me nothing."

"May I ask, Captain," faltered the baron, "whither you are bound, sir? I should not have come aboard, of course, but I am willing and able to pay—"

"We can land anywhere you wish," said the tall man, "but you must know that wherever you land there will be a death cart on the docks and a gallows on a hill. I have no urgent business at the moment—we can simply keep on sailing. As for money, I have no need of it, nor has my crew. You will be well served, Baron, but you will see no man."

The baron shook with an icy chill. Already he was homesick for his broad acres, his dogs and horses, his castle with its bustling servitors, his jolly friends.

"Go below, Baron," said the captain. "There is a storm brewing."

There was a terrific storm that night, and many, many more. The baron lost all track of time. But the days seemed to grow longer and the nights well nigh endless. He had slept so much that he now slept little; he lost interest in the delicious foods served him.

Now and again he would ask how long they had been sailing. At first the answer was weeks, then months. At last, when he could neither eat nor sleep, he staggered on deck to beg the captain to land.

"This life," he said, "is no life at all. I would rather give myself up—even to die. All I ask now is to make a full confession and save my immortal soul!"

"As you wish," said the captain, "but though you pay a hundred—a thousand—priests to say prayers for you, it will be of no avail. It so happens that your soul belongs to me. It became mine when you boarded my ship." He turned, took off his hat, and bowed deeply to the baron. A gust of wind swept the long cloak aside. The light from the lanterns fell full upon the polished horns on the captain's head; upon the scaly tail coiled upon the deck; upon one foot in a great sea boot; the other—it was no foot at all, but a hoof cloven like that of a goat.

The baron, aghast, reeled back against the rail. "Then," he gasped, "you are—you are—"

"I am indeed—I am the Devil himself. Some men call me Satan. Take your choice."

The baron was speechless, but the Devil spoke again. "I will make a bargain with you, Baron. Let us keep on sailing a while; we can throw the dice. It amuses me. If, at the end of a year and a day, you win, you may have back your wretched soul. We will begin at midnight."

With a trembling hand the baron took the dice from the Devil that night. That first night he won—and for several nights thereafter.

He took heart and ate and slept once more. Then the Devil won, with a larger score than all the baron's put together. Night after night they played, with the Devil always keeping an edge ahead. And, doubtless, they still play on.

For three hundred years have come reports of a dark, mysterious vessel, with all sails set, scudding through the waves and fogs of the rough North Sea. And many a seaman has told of seeing two figures on that swift ship, and hearing, across the tumbling waters, sharp and clear, the rattle of dice upon the deck.

HORSES OF THE SEA

THE IRISH say that everything that is upon the land is also in the sea—people and cattle and stout swine and fleet dogs and, above all, fine, swift horses.

Many are the tales of the horses; they have been seen in the sea, on uninhabited islands, on lonely rocks. They have, in the darkness of night, come ashore and eaten bare the oatfields of the peasantry; have been heard galloping, like thunder, along the shores.

This belief in horses of the sea is widespread. Horses with foam-white manes drew across the seas the chariots of the Greek sea god, Poseidon. In later ages France had a small sea horse, his coat black as ebony, lustrous as satin; strangely, he could grow and grow until his shining back was long enough to hold thirty unwary riders, before he plunged into the depths of the sea. The Shetland Islands had the shoopiltie, a seemingly gentle pony which, once having coaxed a rider to mount, would invariably drown him. Scotland had her terrible kelpie; and Iceland a similar sea steed, always described as a splendid dapple-gray. But the cautious Icelanders could always tell this dangerous horse from a real one: his hoofs were reversed.

THE WONDERFUL HORSE

YOUNG Michael was due home from England—in fact, he was overdue—and his Uncle Dermod, having a fine tea with Michael's betrothed, Kitty O'Bannon, and her mother, was uttering dire prophecies, as was his wont.

"I should not," said Uncle Dermod, "eat more of this grand food. For, right this day, my poor nephew may be having none at all." He helped himself generously to the new-baked cakes and accepted fresh tea from Mrs. O'Bannon.

"But Uncle Dermod," protested Kitty, "the boats would be slow, with the many autumn storms, and, perhaps, there was a bigger harvest—"

"For many a long year," persisted Uncle Dermod, "I've seen our young lads go over for the harvesting of the English crops—boatload after boatload of them—eager to earn a penny. And some of them have never seen Ireland again. I never trust the English. So hard up they are for sailors and soldiers, so badly do they treat them, that more than once they have stolen our fine lads and hustled them on their ships in the blackness of night. And off they are forced to go, into strange seas and far-off countries with savage foreigners and fever— Yes—one more cake, Mrs. O'Bannon—a great cook you are indeed. Ah, I'm ever anxious when Michael is late coming."

Kitty's heart grew cold, leaden.

Then, of a sudden, came sounds—running feet, shouts, laughter. A boat must be in. And before she could pull her shawl from the peg, there was Michael in the doorway, bigger than she remembered, sun-browned, with eager, sparkling eyes—and laden with packages.

There was fine China tea for Mrs. O'Bannon, and a warm shawl soft as thistledown, and a fine carved pipe and a mighty tin of tobacco for Uncle Dermod, and for Kitty a tiny box with a ring of stones that sparkled like the stars in heaven.

"It was a great harvest," said Michael, "and I've enough to buy that wee cottage you love, Kitty. And I've brought back china, with little flowers blooming on every plate and cup, and some silver spoons, and—"

"I'm not sure," broke in Uncle Dermod, "I should touch tobacco or a pipe from an enemy land—I'd fear to be disloyal to my own country."

Michael managed not to laugh, and spoke soothingly. "The pipe, Uncle Dermod, is from France, and many a time, through the years, France has been a foe to the English. And the tobacco is from Turkey, and Mother O'Bannon's tea is from China; and even you could scarce have a grudge against those far-off folk you've never seen and never will. Now there is one more thing I want to tell, if you'll give me the space of a breath—I have a horse!"

"Don't tell me," shouted Uncle Dermod, "after breaking your back on the English grain this long summer you've squandered money on a horse!"

"I did not," said Michael patiently. "On the way home the boat stopped at a small island for water, and I found the horse grazing on the beach grass. Likely a survivor of a wrecked ship. There were some racing men on the boat, and all of them agreed this horse had the looks of a great racer—and race him I will. And Kitty will have a dress of shiny silk and golden slippers—"

Uncle Dermod eyed the horse next morning with mingled fear and disfavor. " 'Tis no mortal beast," said he, "but a horse from the deeps of the sea. I laid my hand on his neck and it was cold to the touch."

"It was a chill night," said Michael.

"And," went on Uncle Dermod, "his color is dapple-gray, like I've heard sea horses are like to be—ay, the color of cold wet waves on a stormy sea—and his eyes are pale, like those of a fish."

"I've seen dapple-gray horses before," said Michael, "and so have you. Do you think there's aught uncanny about the butcher's fat horse, and him going his rounds, quiet and faithful as a sheepdog? And the priest too has a dapple-gray, and him sedate as the priest. Besides, I've been told the sea horses are easy to tell, for their hoofs are reversed."

"Some," said Uncle Dermod, "not all. You ride this

great brute and one day he'll go plunging into the sea and you with him."

But day after day Michael rode the horse, and night after night he told Uncle Dermod some wondrous thing the horse had done. "He went over Rafferty's great wall as if it were but a pebble high, and he can run from here to the town while the clock is still striking twelve, and Kitty is sewing me silks of green and gold to wear to the races, and Mrs. O'Bannon is weaving a blanket of golden-colored wool with gay, green shamrocks on both sides—"

But Uncle Dermod would only knock out his pipe and, sighing, go to his room. And his prayers were so loud they would echo through the house. "Save my dear lad from the sea horse and the cold death of the sea. And save young Kitty, who must be daft to be sewing the silks for the races when she is sewing a shroud for the man she loves."

Well, he must talk to her, for if anyone could stop Michael from the racing it would be Kitty O'Bannon.

Uncle Dermod harnessed his small donkey and rode over. Mrs. O'Bannon was out, but Kitty was in, busily sewing, and the floor was strewn with gay scraps of green and gold.

"Is that your wedding gown you're making?" he asked, though he knew better.

"Oh no, Uncle Dermod, these are silks for Michael's first great race. My wedding dress is all done and laid in the chest. Would you care to see it?"

"No," said Uncle Dermod gruffly, "not now. I'd far

rather see you in it when the roses bloom—as we've planned this long time. But I never will. For you'll never wear it." His voice rose and quavered. "Not unless you throw those shining silks on the hot coals and stop Michael from riding the dapple-gray horse. No—no tea; even tea and a crust would choke me this day. I'd hoped, one of these days, to drink tea from the flowery cups in the new cottage—"

"Oh, Uncle Dermod, are you sure there's something strange about the beautiful horse? Aren't you overanxious? I know how you feel, for if anything happened to Michael, I'd be the same as you. There would be no life left for me."

At the door Uncle Dermod turned. "I tell you, Katherine O'Bannon, you must stop Michael. I can do nothing."

Sadly she watched the old man go, and, for the first time, a slight fear struck her. Then she tried the peaked cap on her red curls, and, thinking how handsome Michael would look in it, the little fear was gone.

There seemed but one hope left. Uncle Dermod drove on to the house of the priest. Haltingly, wearily, he told his tale, and quietly, respectfully, the old priest listened. But he could not, did not, believe. And, not believing, it was difficult to talk to Uncle Dermod, but he had to try.

"Dermod," said he, "I've known you many a year, and I know that boy is the very core of your heart. But there are no horses in the sea save the tiny sea horses, which are not horses at all, and there are no mermaids or seals with the power of speech, though often their cries have a strangely human sound. Forget these old tales; forget the fears; there is naught in the sea but tasty fish for the eating and pretty shells for the edging of flowerbeds. Here's a bite of sugar for your faithful donkey, since you'll take naught for yourself. And may peace go with you."

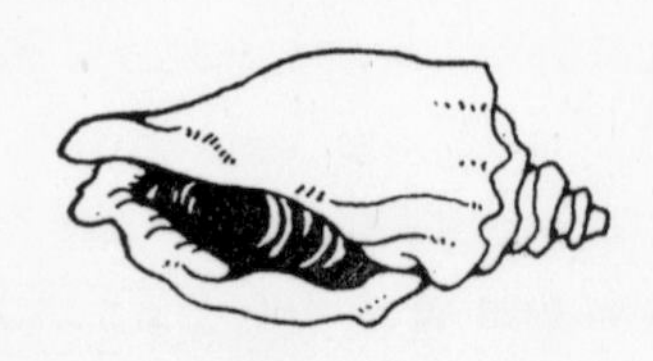

But Uncle Dermod felt many fears when Michael went off to the first big race, and he could feel no joy when the news came of how the dapple-gray horse had won against all competitors. He could show no interest in all the prizes and the pictures in the papers.

Then away went Michael again, and it was the same tale over at the best races in England. Even the London papers were full of praise for the swift, high-leaping gray horse.

"I'll take him to America next," bragged Michael, with shining eyes.

"Will you take him to Kilderry the coming week?" asked Uncle Dermod. "To the big fair? The whole village is going, and, I hear, more folk from many miles around."

"No," said Michael slowly, " 'twould not be a sporting thing to race my horse against any of the entries hereabouts. They would scarce see a hair of his tail, so fast he is. In fact, I'll not go to the fair at all. Kitty and I have plans to look over the cottage and see what's to be done there, and I may turn over some ground for the making of a garden, which is her heart's desire. We figured that with everyone gone to the fair we could do it with no advice and no prying eyes. The plan suited her—she said she'd a bit more to finish on the lace for her wedding cap and she'd promised to take Halloran's little lame boy for the day."

"Mind you give my donkey his oats," said Uncle Dermod, "and his draught of water. I am bid to go to the fair with the priest and Mrs. O'Bannon."

"Behind a dangerous dapple-gray steed," said Michael, with mirth in his eyes.

But Uncle Dermod made no answer.

The whole village went to the fair, all save Kitty and Michael and Hugh Halloran's little lame boy whom Kitty had offered to take for the day, that his mother might enjoy a rare outing.

So it was from young Hughie Halloran that Uncle Dermod and Mrs. O'Bannon and the priest heard the terrible tale, they being first home from the fair.

Hughie met them down the road, his little face drawn from the pain of walking, and red from weeping. "Michael was racing the gray horse on the shore," he sobbed, "and of a sudden the horse turned to the sea. I saw Michael striving to turn him, but so wild he was, rearing and plunging, that not even Michael could hold him. Straight into the waves he went, and under them. I could not run

for Kitty, only hobble. Hours we stood on the shore, but we never saw them again; only Michael's green and gold cap came in on the rising tide. Kitty was white and shaking, and for a long time she said nothing; she just stood there, turning the gay cap over and over in her hands.

"Then she cried out of a sudden, 'Wherever he's gone, he'll be racing the horse, and in all countries he'd want his cap with the colors of Ireland upon it. I must take it to him!' I clung to her skirt, but there was no holding her. Into the next great wave she went; just once I saw a glint of her red hair, and then she was gone."

Uncle Dermod died with the coming of dawn. All night the priest had sat beside his bed, knowing the end was near.

"Dermod, my friend," begged the priest for the tenth time, "take back the wicked words you said this afternoon when you heard about Michael—that there was no mercy in the hand of God. Take them back before you go—for going you are; the tide is fast ebbing."

Uncle Dermod smiled. "I will," said he, "on one condition—that you take back the false words you said to me many moons ago."

"False words?" said the old priest, pained and puzzled.

"Ay," said Uncle Dermod, "false words—that there were no horses in the sea."

THE MOON-CHILD

A little lonely child am I
　That hath not any soul:
God made me as the homeless wave,
　That has no goal.

A seal my father was, a seal
That once was man:
My mother loved him tho' he was
'Neath mortal ban.

He took a wave and drownèd her,
She took a wave and lifted him:
And I was born where shadows are
In sea-depths dim.

All through the sunny blue-sweet hours
I swim and glide in waters green:
Never by day the mournful shores
By me are seen.

But when the gloom is on the wave
A shell unto the shore I bring:
And then upon the rocks I sit
And plaintive sing.

I have no playmate but the tide
The seaweed loves with dark brown eyes:
The night-waves have the stars for play,
For me but sighs.

—Fiona Macleod

THE SEALS

FROM the earliest days seals have been regarded with awe and superstition. Their uncanny intelligence, their strange cries, often nearly human, made many believe they were enchanted mortals, condemned, for some evil deed, to dwell in animal form in the chill waters.

Many are the tales: that the seals are the souls of the soldiers of Pharaoh's army, which perished in the Red Sea; that they are the souls of the wicked drowned in the Great Flood. In the northern islands men told of a great seal, seen throughout many centuries. Black Angus they called him, but they did not think that to be his true name—they thought him that treacherous apostle, Judas, in dark disguise.

Of mortals who married with the seal folk, when in human form, the reports are legion—and of their children, often handsome but at times sullen and quick to anger, and never happy away from the sight and sound of the sea.

THE WIFE OF BJORN BRYN

BOTH Bjorn Bryn's mother and father had protested about his going fishing the night before his grandfather's will was to be read. But, stubbornly, he had gone.

"Tomorrow is like any other day," he had protested, "and I understand the fish are running off the western headland in great shoals, like the sands of the sea."

"Wills are very important," his mother had said sharply. "They sometimes change the whole of one's destiny."

So now Bjorn sat uncomfortably in the overcrowded little office of the lawyer, very cramped and exceedingly sleepy, while the lawyer's tallow-faced young clerk fussily and importantly shuffled a sheaf of papers and the relatives whispered among themselves.

"Young Bjorn was ever the old man's favorite," came an echoing whisper. "He may get everything."

"But," came another whisper, "Bjorn is the second generation. I'd think things would first go to the old man's own children and his brother and sisters. Then, later, Bjorn might inherit."

Silence fell as the lawyer entered.

Quietly, impressively, he read the brief, simple will—certain goodly sums of money to the old man's sons and daughters and to his brother and sisters, to be left in turn to their children as they saw fit. And to his grandson, Bjorn, his boat, his house, and "all which it contains."

Strangely enough, everyone was satisfied. No one wanted the old house, staunch and roomy though it was. It was in too lonely a place. That is, no one but Bjorn wanted it. He had always loved that house when his grandfather lived in it; he had spent much time there.

He was jubilant that night. "You will come there to live with me?" he asked his parents. "It is a much larger house than this, and a wide view of the water—and—"

Both of them shook their heads.

"It is much too far from the village," said his mother. "Your father likes to see his friends, and I mine. Surely, my dear son, you are not thinking of living there! Nothing but the wailing of the wind and the eternal screaming of the gulls and the barking of the seals upon the rocks! I—I never told you, but your grandmother ran away from there, and she was very odd in her mind for a long time after. And your grandfather had one housekeeper after another, until he got old Granny Gioga, who stayed until he died."

"I always liked that house," said Bjorn. "I think I will like it now. I still remember the old tales my grandfather used to tell me—"

"What sort of tales?" asked Olaf, Bjorn's father.

"Oh, different kinds—of some of the smugglers and pirates who now and again asked permission to anchor briefly in the cove—most gentlemanly he said they were.

They would offer bottles and big demijohns of fine wines and brandies to pay for a steaming cup of simple tea, and shining gems for a bite of sizzling bacon and a fresh cake hot from the coals. And good porridge—they'd give anything for a bowl of that, so weary they were of ship's fare."

"I have always wondered," said Bjorn's mother, looking reproachfully at her husband, "where your father got so much money."

Bjorn broke in defensively. "Grandfather never took anything. He said he would have offered the same hospitality to any man long upon the waters, and longing for a bite of fresh hot food upon the land. And he never asked their professions—he just guessed, for some of the vessels bore neither flag nor name. But he said they did leave gifts on his doorstep, and he could do nothing about that, for those ships were always gone—"

"Troublous times, those," said Olaf hastily, "most troublous times. A natural hatred toward the grasping, luxury-loving monarchs and nobles, good men imprisoned because of politics—it turned many an honest man to smuggling and to piracy."

Seeing his mother's face, Bjorn changed the subject. "And when I was younger," he resumed, "he used to tell me tales of the sea man, the Neck, who could teach music to mortals. You remember Grandfather used to sing and play—"

"I doubt he learned that from a sea monster," said Bjorn's mother. "I believe he had lessons from a man from Copenhagen or—"

"And," went on Bjorn bravely, "he also used to tell me of the seal folk, many of whom are half human and can shed their seal skins and walk as mortals on the land; and of the mermaids and mermen, who can do the same; and of human folk who have married them—and he said too that these seal women and mermaids are slim as reeds and of exceeding beauty—"

"Merciful Heaven!" exclaimed his mother. "You don't—you can't believe such tales! Have I not taken you to the Christian church since you could barely walk?"

"Of course I don't believe these nursery tales," said Bjorn, "but I enjoyed them as a child. Anyway I am going to live in my grandfather's house."

"You will never get a wife who will," said his mother.

"I don't want any wife," said Bjorn.

"A wife is a good thing," said Olaf, "to welcome you home in the evenings; to have ready a steaming, savory supper; and—" he ended somewhat lamely, seeing his wife's eyes upon him, "to—er—to—love and to cherish—" He paused, mopped his brow. "You are twenty-eight years old, my son."

Bjorn shrugged his broad shoulders. "Any housekeeper can light a fire and fix a supper; that is all the welcome I need. As for the love, that must wait until it comes—if ever. I am going to bed."

"I have an idea," said Olaf. "Perhaps we can persuade Bjorn to go inland to my brother Svend's farm for a while, while you clean the house. Perhaps, since you are so set upon it, he might meet a nice girl."

"There are plenty of nice girls here," said his wife, "but he says one is too fat, another too high-colored. I do wish your father had not told him all those tales of sea women 'slim as reeds'! Fine wives they would make for fishermen!"

"I wonder," said Olaf, changing the subject abruptly, "that clause in the will—about the house and all that it contains. Lawyer Larsen said that my father made a point of having that phrase most heavily underlined—"

"So far as I know," said his wife, "there is nothing in the house save the usual furniture, and doubtless, by now, plenty of dust, cobwebs, and mice. Oh yes, there are some old chests and boxes in the storeroom; the locks are rusted and Granny Gioga says she has never seen any keys."

"Old love letters," suggested Olaf, smiling, and his wife smiled back.

"Laugh, if you will, Olaf," said she, "but it is time Bjorn had a wife, and, as he grows older, he will be glad of stalwart sons to aid him. Anyway, I think your idea of sending him inland to his Uncle Svend's farm, before he settles in that lonely spot, a most excellent one."

But Bjorn thought otherwise. "I know nothing of farming," he said next morning. "And I want to fix my house."

"You know still less of cleaning and housekeeping," said his mother.

"Very well, I will not interfere with your putting the

house in order—I will be most grateful. But I also want to make some repairs on my grandfather's boat. I don't know just why you want to send me away, but I am not going. I hate the inland country with its walls and"—his brows were close-knit now, and his mouth grim—"and every flock of lambs in a green pasture puts me in mind of the white foam on sea water, and every calling bird is the gulls' cry in my ears!"

And out the door he went, and a blast of sea wind blew in, chilling the room.

So Bjorn Bryn went to live in his grandfather's house on the lonely cliff, and Granny Gioga went with him.

"I am aging," she said, "but perhaps I may last until you find yourself a fine young wife."

"You will have to live a long, long time, Granny," Bjorn said, and off he went to his boat.

He was late coming home that night, and very tired, and as he anchored in the little cove he thought he saw figures dancing on the shore and heard singing. He rubbed his eyes. Ah, no—merely seals; they were diving into the water. What he had thought were white figures must have been moonlight on the rocks, and the music but the lapping of waves.

Half asleep, he stumbled up the steep path of the cliff. His foot touched something, and he picked it up—a sealskin, singularly small and soft. Then he saw her, crouched by the foam of the water—a girl with long brown hair, her slim shoulders shaken with sobs. She raised soft brown eyes streaming with tears. Piteously she

begged for her sealskin. He put it around her but he would not, could not, let her go. She seemed unable to stand, so he carried her to the house, laid her on a bed.

Granny Gioga came swiftly at his call.

"Heat some blankets, Granny. I will build a fire, but give me the sealskin."

And the sealskin he hid.

"So!" said Granny Gioga next morning. "So!" He laid a gold piece on the table.

"I don't want it, Master Bryn. Send her back to the sea! I am an old woman; I have seen such things before. This is sorrow for her today—dire sorrow. It may be sorrow for you tomorrow, and for all the years to come."

For many days the girl stood looking out of first one window and then another; for many nights she sobbed herself to sleep. When Bjorn was out fishing she searched frantically for her sealskin. Bjorn saw her seldom—just an occasional glimpse of a flitting, forlorn little figure clad in some of Granny Gioga's drab clothing.

Then, one evening, Granny Gioga met him halfway down the path to the cove. His heart almost stopped when he saw her. "No, no, Master Bjorn, she has not gone; she is asleep. She is worn out hunting for her little sealskin. But, while I was out for a moment, she found the keys to the chests in the storeroom, and opened them, hoping the skin might be hidden in one. You see, your grandfather tried, as he lay on his deathbed, to tell me about the keys, but it was too late. The child took nothing out; she was not even interested. She only wanted her sealskin."

Late that night Bjorn and Granny Gioga sat in the storeroom, staring into the open chests; then at each other.

"Will you read your grandfather's letter to me again, Master Bjorn?"

They had found the letter in a chest—and a beautiful old shawl, neatly folded, and under the shawl a shining treasure of gold coins.

Granny Gioga's eyes were wet. "Of course I was faithful to him—he was a good and kindly master."

Bjorn was dazed. He would pick up one thing from one chest, something else from another, drop them back. Silver candlesticks, bowls, jewels, strings of pearls, coins too numerous to count.

His wide blue eyes sought Granny Gioga's face, and she was smiling. "Master Bjorn," she said, "you look, this night, as you used to look when you were a young boy and your grandfather told you tales of the smugglers and the pirates."

He sighed. "Ah, Granny, would I were so carefree, so happy as then!"

"The girl has changed much, of late, Master Bjorn. She cries no more, she helps me about the house, in my tiny garden. She has learned to spin, to sew, to knit. It is only now and then she hunts for her sealskin. Perhaps—"

Bjorn shook his head. All the next week, alone on his boat, he fought between his love and his pity. And the pity won. He must not keep this wild thing caged any longer.

That night he gave the sealskin to Granny Gioga. "Put it on her bed after she has gone to sleep, and I will leave the lock off the door."

Granny Gioga hesitated. "Master Bjorn," she said, "the socks and the fine-wrought muffler you thanked me for—she made them—and the little cakes in your lunch basket. And she made the pretty little dress she came to supper in the other night—and braided her beautiful hair, and put the tiny shells in it—"

"I noticed the shells," he said gruffly.

"And now it is she who polishes the great door lantern each day, and lights it at dusk, and stands watching for your sail. I am not sure, but—"

"But Granny, you yourself said—"

"I know, but I could be mistaken. I am not sure but what this dear child is trying to answer a question you have never asked. I don't think you even know her name. It is Mari."

When Bjorn woke next morning there was no sign of

the girl. But he heard Granny Gioga singing softly in the kitchen. When she brought in his breakfast she was smiling.

"The little maid," she said, "is working in the garden. Yes, Master Bjorn, I put the sealskin on her bed, as you bade me. I don't know where she put it. I don't know anything, except that men can be very, very stupid."

Well, Mari had her sealskin; Bjorn had done what he considered right. Each evening when he came home, each morning when he woke, he expected to find her gone. He began to feel woefully tired with a weariness he had never felt before. For the waves lapping against the boat seemed to be an eternal echo of Granny's words: *Men are very, very stupid. . . . Trying to answer a question you have never asked.*

After supper one night, muttering some excuse, he went down to his boat. Actually, he wished to think, to make up his mind.

When he came back, Mari was spinning by the fire. She usually disappeared right after supper; sometimes she did not come to supper at all.

"Mari—" he said, "no—please don't go; I want to talk to you."

He went on with difficulty, flushing under his heavy tan, stammering a little, twisting his strong, sun-bronzed hands. "You know, don't you, how I feel? You know—you must know—that I love you? You—you have your sealskin back, but—"

The spinning wheel whirred into silence, but the girl did not look up. She stared into the fire, and her voice was very low. "Master Bjorn, when I was—well, what I was—I would often lie on the rocks in the evening and smell the fragrant smoke from the hearth fires in the cottages and see the lanterns lit at the doorways in the blue dusk, and see the sails coming over the rim of the sea and the womenfolk running out to welcome their men home. And I would often have a strange longing for the life of the land. I could not understand it, until my mother told me—told me that my father was a fisherman, but—but she went back to the sea. And I was born in the sea."

She went to the door, opened it, and stood looking out. The sound of the waves seemed to pour in, icy cold, flooding the warm room. She closed the door and came back, holding out slim hands to the fire. "I love this house," she said slowly, "and, sometimes, I was cold in the sea. May I have a little time to think, Master Bjorn?"

"Of course, but not *Master* Bjorn."

"It is what Granny Gioga says."

"Bjorn," he said firmly.

How beautiful she was, how gentle—and yet, her face, as she had stood, looking out at the dark water . . . ! He had little hope.

She turned to go.

"Mari, shall I ask you again sometime, or will you just tell me?"

"You will know," she said. "Good night—Bjorn."

Sadly he went to bed, to uneasy slumber.

Once he was almost sure he heard the heavy door quietly open and close. Perhaps it was only the wind. Well, there was no more he could do.

He awoke sick at heart. He rose wearily, dressed like a man in a dream, groping in the dark room. It was not yet dawn.

Her words came back to him: *You will know*. He did know—he was sure, now, he had heard that door. He would never see her again.

Suddenly the sun rose, flooding the room with golden light. And Bjorn Bryn started, stared, unbelieving. On the foot of his bed lay the little sealskin.

KIRSTEN McVURICH

THE MOTHER SUPERIOR seemed, at first glance, a stern woman, so tall and straight she was in her severe habit. But with a second look you saw a rare tenderness in her face and felt it in her gentle manner. And this was the true picture of her, for she had a real affection in her heart for her nuns, and especially for the young ones.

So when a fisherman, Ivor McVurich, brought his daughter, Kirsten, to enter the convent, the Mother Superior hesitated. "She is very, very young," she said.

"Yes, Mother, but that is the reason I brought her. She is motherless, and no womenfolk among our kith and kin free to look out for her. And I am much away."

The Mother Superior gazed long at young Kirsten, standing by the window, her long hair ruddy-gold in the sunlight, her eyes wide and frightened as a child's. "Does she wish it?"

"She has not said," answered Ivor. "She is an obedient daughter."

"Well," said the Mother Superior, "I will take her, keep her here, but as yet not even as a novice, merely as a ward of the Holy Church. She will be taught the services and the prayers and the arts of weaving and the making of simples for the sick—all such things—and, also, the glory of serving our good Lord in Heaven. But she is over-young; in a few years she can decide for herself."

"I thank you, Mother Gilda," said Ivor, rising to go.

But Kirsten ran forward and flung her arms about him. "You will—you can come to see me?" Her eyes sought the Mother Superior's.

"Of course he may," she answered.

The slim arms tightened around Ivor's neck. "And you will remember to take off your sea-soaked clothing and dry it with care, and you will cook the porridge well before eating? And you will remember what the priest told you—ever to take a pinch of salt and a drop of holy water when you go upon the sea? And you will turn back from the waters if you meet the things of ill omen? Promise me that. And—and you will remember never to make mention of me while upon the waters, please—"

"Yes, Kirsten, I will remember all these things," said Ivor. "And now, good-by, my child."

But she could not say good-by. She stood at the window, watching her father's stalwart figure go down to the shore, watched the sails go up in the old fishing boat, watched the boat out of sight.

When she turned from the window her eyes were brimming with tears.

"Sit down, little sister," said the Mother Superior gently. "Your father wished you to come here; you must make the best of it. We will teach you many things—fine weaving, so you can make warm shirts for your father—"

The tears were drying now, but to distract her still further the Mother Superior went on. "And now, Kirsten, would you care to tell me what you meant when you warned your father against ill omens, and to make no mention of you when on the water?"

"Yes, Mother. It is ill luck when you go a-fishing"—the girl flushed suddenly, but went on—"to meet a man of the church or a barefoot woman, or to see a hare scudding through the mists of dawn. All the seagoing folk of Scotland know that. There will be no fish to be caught, and danger besides. One should turn back, wait for another day."

"And not mentioning you upon the water?"

"Ah, that is another thing—of another land. My mother was of Ireland. And my grandfather said that while on the peril of the waves there should be no mention of a human or a four-footed beast with red hair. My hair is red. And he recalled the strange drowning of a fine young man for no reason anyone could see save that the live-long day he had talked of nothing but a rousing racing foxhunt he had been on the day before. There is nothing so dire as the mention of a fox."

Long that night Mother Gilda knelt in prayer upon the cold hard stones of the little chapel. She must, with both her mind and her heart, try to do the right thing for this wild, motherless young girl. But what was the right thing? All the womanly anxiety about her father's wet clothing, the cooking of the porridge? Was this girl destined to be a nun or not? Perhaps she was more fitted for the warm red glow of the hearth fire than the pale white flame of the holy candle? Long ago Mother Gilda had given up an earthly love for a holy one. She had not regretted it, but she remembered, and understood.

As if she had actually heard a voice saying, "Wait," she rose from her knees, comforted. At the door she found Sister Bridget waiting for her.

"She ate as a child," said Sister Bridget simply, "now she sleeps as a child. But,"—she hesitated—"her prayers were strange. Very scattered little prayers—hardly like our own. She did pray for her father, upon the sea, but she looked long out of the window, watching the seals upon the rocks, and then she knelt again and prayed—that was very clear—for the salvation of the seals.

" 'Poor souls,' she said, and her wide eyes were full of sorrow, 'once they had the shelter of homes and the sweet warmth of food and fire, and now, forever and forever, they have but the icy water and the lashing winds upon their bodies and the salt in their mouths. There must have been dire sins, indeed, which doomed them to this.' "

Mother Gilda sighed. "This looks like a hard task," she said, "and a long one. You will help me, Bridget, my friend?"

"Yes, Mother, in every way I can."

Kirsten was slow at the weaving and sewing, but at last a fine soft shirt was completed for her father. She seemed far happier in the gardens, and under her strong slim fingers plants throve. With infinite care and singular skill she arranged the flowers for the altar in the little chapel.

Once Mother Gilda and Sister Bridget found tiny bowls of flowers in their bare cells. "Dear child," the Mother Superior said gently, "we are not supposed to have flowers for ourselves."

Kirsten's wide eyes grew puzzled, troubled. Then she shook her mane of red hair. "There would be no flowers did not the Lord God will it," she said. "And I cannot think He would claim all for Himself—no, ah no—but to brighten also the lives of His faithful servants."

There seemed to be no good answer to this, so the flowers remained. And, from time to time, more came.

"May I gather some shells to edge the beds where the little herbs grow?" Kirsten asked one day.

"Of course, my child," Mother Gilda agreed.

Not long after, Kirsten appeared one day with a scallop shell hung around her neck on a slender thread. "It is a symbol, is it not, Mother, of those who crossed to the Holy Land upon the dangerous seas?"

"Yes, it is," answered Mother Gilda, "the pilgrims. But—but you are not a pilgrim; you have not crossed that sea."

"No," said the girl slowly, "not that sea, truly—only the perilous sea of my own soul."

Months later Ivor McVurich came, and Kirsten, with trembling hands, laid the beautiful shirt upon his knees and sat at his feet, gazing up into his face, as might a faithful dog. She begged to go with him to the boat, and she was a long time coming back.

One of the sisters reported that she had seen Kirsten

swimming, swift as an otter or a salmon, after her father left. Another reported she had seen the girl clamber upon the rocks in the cove and talk to the gathering seals.

Mother Gilda's fears increased, but they were dispelled when Kirsten came in. She was very quiet, somber. "I have decided," she said. "When the great man of the Church comes again I wish him to cut off my hair. I will become a nun."

"Did your father urge it, Kirsten?"

"He said nothing; it is my own wish. I have reasons."

It was a long time before the bishop came, and the Mother Superior was secretly glad, for she was still uncertain of the proper destiny for this strange girl. At times Kirsten was so quiet, so serene, she seemed already a dedicated nun; at other times she would race along the beach, her red-gold hair flying, singing strange little wordless songs—a wild thing, indeed. At these times, she often came back barely in time for evensong.

It was hard to reprove this childlike girl, but once the good Mother did. "Come in a little earlier, Kirsten, in time to wash the sea water from your hands and smooth your hair."

"I could not tonight, Mother. The seals were late in coming in—and—he was later."

The Mother Superior started, paled. *"He?"*

"Ay, the big seal. He expects me to be upon the shore or on the rocks. Poor, poor soul! It is for his sake I must be a nun, that I may say the right words to give him comfort. I pray, but mine are halting prayers. I wish to speak as did the white monk, Colum, when he preached to the seals—that white monk who first brought the message of Christ to the northern isles, sending the evil Druids back into their dark forests."

"You think Colum preached to the seals?"

"My grandfather said he did, and that the seals were comforted. They were sure so merciful a man as the Lord Jesus would, one day, forgive them their sins, and that once more they would, as humans, walk upon the land, and sit by the warm hearth fires. Then the young girls would gather garlands for their hair, and the young men would have fair green acres to till and gentle warm flocks to tend. Ah, Mother, it is cold, bitter cold, in the sea!"

At last the bishop came, and to him the Mother Superior poured forth all her doubts and fears about Kirsten.

"Perhaps," said the bishop thoughtfully, "it would be well to wait a while."

But Kirsten was insistent. She pled, wept. Without a tremor she saw all her glorious red hair fall about her feet. She ran a slender hand over her shaven head and smiled. When she donned the nun's white habit her face was radiantly beautiful.

And for a long time she seemed, in all ways, to be changed. She walked sedately upon the cliff with one of her sister nuns; she went no more upon the beach. She still worked in the garden, but spent more time within the convent walls, at the weaving, lace-making, even embroidery.

The Mother Superior relaxed.

Then, one midnight, Sister Bridget came to the Mother Superior's room. Her hands shook as she set down the candle; her face was ashen. "I did not tell you," she said. "I have talked and talked to Kirsten, but this last month time and again she has gone upon the beach after all the convent was sleeping. And look!"

The Mother Superior looked from the narrow window. The beach shone silver under the full moon; the sky was spangled with a multitude of stars. Kirsten's white robe seemed luminous in the light. She was sitting upon the sand; one slim white hand lay upon a huge dark object at her side. The dark object stirred, raised a head. The Mother Superior shuddered. Clearly she saw an immense seal, his coat shining with the sea water, his white tusks gleaming.

Mother Gilda reached for her cloak, fragments of Kirsten's strange little utterances racing through her mind: *The great seal. . . . I must give him comfort. . . . All the seals will walk again upon the land, their sins forgiven. . . .*

"Not tonight," begged Sister Bridget. "You are too weary. Wait until tomorrow; Kirsten is coming up the path now."

Mother Gilda watched the girl the next day, but her lovely face showed no sign of distress or of guilt. Long she bent over the weaving; carefully she arranged the altar flowers. There seemed to be no time for Mother Gilda to speak, but tonight she must. She knelt before the little altar, praying for guidance.

When Kirsten slipped out, no one ever knew. And no one saw her on the beach. Sister Bridget reported her asleep in her bed as the bells tolled midnight.

It was in the chill light of dawn that Mother Gilda awoke, aware of a commotion somewhere—men's gruff voices talking, talking; the frightened, birdlike voices of the nuns. Where were they? Oh, at the door in the sea wall. She hastened out.

Sister Bridget held Kirsten's sea-soaked habit. She could not speak.

Finally one of the men did. "We saw the young sister, Mother; she went in on the high tide. We have searched all night, but we have found no trace of her." Then he dug into his pocket. "But this we found." He brought out a long string of beads with a cross, rubbed it carefully on his rough coat sleeve, and held it out. "I am sorry, it has a bit of stain upon it—a bloodstain. The sea water will not wholly take it off."

He looked at all the frightened nuns, and the Mother Superior signaled for all of them but Sister Bridget to retire. She felt close to fainting.

The man hesitated, twisting his cap in his hands.

"Do you think," quavered Mother Gilda, "that the young nun was killed upon those jagged rocks?"

"I don't know, Mother, but I think not. The blood-stain was not from her, but from the great seal we wounded; the cross was around his neck. All of us saw it —it fell off, floated, when he dived deep."

The sun was blotted out for Mother Gilda. On this brilliant day she seemed to be in a gray void, haunted and terrifying. With an effort she held out her hand, felt the wet cross in her palm. "I thank you," she said. "Do you think you killed the seal?"

The men looked at one another warily. "No, good Mother, no one will ever kill that seal. He is meant to live on and on—doomed and sorrow-stricken—unless—now—the young nun's cross has saved him."

"Am I mad, or are you?" whispered Mother Gilda. She felt Sister Bridget's warm strong arms about her as all the world turned black.

"Maybe we all are," came the man's voice, very low. "But there are many who believe that seal is no seal—he is the betrayer of the Lord Jesus—Judas."

STRANGE FOLK OF THE SEA

FOR LONG ages the belief in men and women of the sea was almost universal. The names differed; the descriptions were similar. Most of them were human in form above the waist, with fish tails below, but some had human shape.

Mermaids were prevalent along the northern coasts of Europe. Greece had the Nereids, Scandinavia had the handsome and kindly Havemand and the Havrue, beautiful but treacherous. Ireland had her merrows—the men of unbelievable ugliness, the women of almost incredible loveliness.

There has been much disagreement about the color of the hair of the sea women. Some contended that it was green or brown like the seaweed, but the most popular fancy was that it was a pure and shimmering gold.

The Germans had the Undines, who by marrying infatuated young men of the mortal race gained immortal souls, but in payment were no longer free from human pains and sorrows. Germany had, also, the Nix and Nixie, who were often seen upon the land, even trading at the village markets. They were ever in neat peasant costume; but, could you persuade the Nix to laugh, you would know him, for he had fish teeth, of a brilliant green. And the Nixie had always a tiny wet spot—on her dress, her apron, the corner of her kerchief—betraying the watery home from which she came.

The sirens, sometimes confused with mermaids, were very different. Part woman, part bird, they dwelt upon the high cliffs overlooking the blue Mediterranean and lured many a mariner to shipwreck and death by the sweetness of their singing.

"Fisher, hast thou seen the mermaid combing her hair, yellow as gold, by the noontide sun, at the edge of the water?"

"I have seen the fair mermaid. I have also heard her singing; her songs were plaintive as the waves."

—from an old ballad of Brittany

MARTIN GROGAN AND THE MERROW

"MY SON Martin," Mrs. Grogan often said, with pride, "was a merry smiling baby in the cradle and he could scarce walk when he was bringing in little twigs for the fires and setting out milk for the cats to spare me the stooping, and only eight when he was helping his father with the digging of the fields and the planting and minding the small flock of sheep we have."

And Patrick Grogan would nod in proud agreement.

But no one, young or old, ever resented the Grogans' pride in Martin, for the entire village felt the same way. You could hear his praises around hearth fires in cottages, in the lanes, in The Bells of Ireland, the one tavern in the little town.

There was quite a crowd there one frosty Saturday night and, somehow, the talk turned upon Martin.

"He is now twenty-seven years old," said the old doctor, slowly sipping the mug of ale he allowed himself once a week, "and it seems but yesterday that I borned him."

"Do you know," said a fisherman, "it may sound a queer thing, but never does Martin go in a boat but there is a fine catch of fish. I asked him did he carry some sort of charm. He shook his head and laughed. But my nephew in

America writes that the fishermen in New England carry a pebble from the nest of a fishhawk or a bone from the head of a cod. He has promised to send me some—I see no harm in them."

"And no good either," said another fisherman, "and I doubt the priest would approve. Martin, I'm sure, believes in none of these silly things."

"Martin is not only good at the fishing," interrupted an old man, "but his father, Patrick, says he has a way with crops. And I myself know he has a way with animals. Didn't I have trouble with my donkey and him refusing to budge and me cutting peat until I was sore in every limb, when along came Martin, and the donkey willing to haul as soon as that young man spoke in his ear."

"And me," said an old shepherd, "with my sheep scattered over the wide world and the dogs barking and chasing in vain, until Martin happened by and in no time at all the whole flock was as a drift of white heather around his two feet and all my troubles ended. The sheep dogs came to him, too, and savage as they can sometimes be, they licked his hands, as if trying to thank him for his help to them."

"Did he not ride the Squire's fine horse in a dozen races and win against all comers?" said a young man. "Ay, even the great horses sent on the boat from England? And he is ever first in the leaping and the hurling—"

"Ah, fishing, animals, hurling, leaping," broke in the handsome young barmaid with contempt. "You've not said a half of it. Mr. Grogan has more than that to him.

How about the way, despite his size and strength, he can dance a jig or a reel as light as a butterfly, and how about the sweet voice he has for singing and his fine memory for the old songs? 'Tis these things women think on. That foreign man who was here a fortnight back told me how in eastern lands a man can have as many wives as he chooses —a harem, he named it—and I told him there was a man right here could have every unwed maid in the village if he liked, though it is not our custom."

"I don't think," said a burly sea captain from Scotland, "it is necessary to have more than one wife. Cannot one woman cook a bite of fish and a few oaten bannocks for supper? Myself, I'd not care for a whole household of women, likely quarreling among themselves and with you into the bargain. And think of the money. If one had a new bonnet or shawl, all the rest would set up a clamor for the same."

"I recommend no heathen harem," said the barmaid, very sharp, and slamming down the tankards. "All I said was that Mr. Grogan could have any he chose. But he chooses no one. He takes one girl to a fair, another to the races, another to a dance. I figure he is no marrying man."

Such was Martin Grogan until—well, no one ever knew exactly what happened, but Martin changed overnight.

"It was on Midsummer Eve the change came on him," said Mrs. Grogan tearfully, to her closest friend, Mrs. O'Connor. "He said he was going to the boat a short while, then to the bonfires and the dancing, but he was seen by no one. About midnight he came in, with his eyes sunk deep in his head and he would take neither bite nor sup, and straightway went to bed. Now, he dutifully helps his father with the fishing and farming, but he scarce smiles at all and he sings and dances no more. No, he's not home all the time. Each night he goes out, but no one has seen him save some fishermen out late and they said he was sitting lonesome on the shore.

"I'd think he was love-struck, for that sickness can come even to the most sensible, but I know he has looked at no girl here, and he has never been long away to visit another country, unless it was that fishing trip up the Cornwall coast. Well, I mustn't tire you with my troubles, Norah, after the fine comforting tea you've given me."

Now if Martin had gone to join the other young folk, gathering boughs of blossom and building bonfires, this strange thing might never have happened. But Martin insisted on going by his father's boat to do a bit of work so all would be ready for an early start in the morning.

"Ah, don't bother tonight, Martin," protested his father. "There's little to do. Go join your friends at the merrymaking."

"I will later," said Martin, "but the moon is bright as the dawn, and there's one net I want to see to, and a fish barrel with a loose rim. It looks like a fine day for fishing tomorrow. We should start with sun-up."

He had not been half an hour on the boat when he heard a small sound and saw little white hands appear on the gunwale. And then just above the edge a head appeared and Martin found himself staring into the face of the fairest woman he had ever seen. On her head was a close cap of shining feathers, her long hair was pale gold, her mouth like coral, and her eyes green as the sea.

He found his voice with an effort. "Won't you come aboard?" he asked, reaching out a bronzed hand.

"No, no, I like it better in the water, but sing that song you were singing when I came."

So Martin sang, and in a few minutes the fair woman was singing with him and her voice was sweeter than any he had ever heard in his lifetime.

From the shore came singing, too, and a sudden light from the new-kindled bonfires.

"What are they doing?" she asked.

"An old custom," he answered. "On Midsummer Eve—come, I'll take you there."

She shook her head. "I'm not properly dressed. In fact, I have on nothing at all."

The wind blew back her long hair and he saw the gleam of her wet shoulders, white as sea foam.

"Where do you live?" he asked.

"At the bottom of the sea," she answered.

And then he knew. He was face to face with one of the sea women, one of the merrows, in whom he had never believed.

Her hands slipped from the gunwale. He tried to catch one.

"Wait, wait!" he cried impulsively, but again she shook her head.

"I must get back before he misses me," she said, and dived deep out of sight.

Night after night Martin haunted the shore, or took the boat out, hoping to see her again. Desperately he tried to stop looking, to forget the whole matter. But he could not. Who was that "he" she spoke of and seemed to fear?

A wave of jealousy and anger swept over him and he buried his face in his hands and moaned aloud. "I, Martin Grogan, with never a heartache in my life, in love with a sea maid, and jealous of a man or a fish or whatever he is that I've never seen!"

Just then he saw something black at the edge of the water. It came higher and higher, and Martin saw it was a huge cocked hat, and under it the ugliest face he had ever beheld. The creature had green hair and long sharp green teeth, a very red nose and tiny eyes like those of a pig. It lifted a short arm much like a fin.

"I'll thank you, Martin Grogan, never to speak again to the sea woman you saw some moons back. Time and time again my lobster cages have been turned over. She is supposed to attend to them, not waste time singing songs with you, a stranger."

"Is she—your wife?" asked Martin.

"That's my affair, and mine alone," croaked the creature, and away he went, swimming swiftly with his short, stout fins, and the big cocked hat bobbing like a dark cork on the water.

But the next night the little white hands came up on the gunwale and the lovely strange face looked up at Martin and he saw she had been weeping.

"He is not my husband," said she. "It is so planned but I do not choose. As for the lobster cages, I tipped them over and I will keep on tipping them, for those are not lobsters in the cages but the souls of human beings, of drowned sailors." She burst into low sobbing. "You see," she said, "my mother was of the sea folk and she went back to the sea when I was a wee child, taking me with her. But my father was a Christian man of the land, so my heart goes out to these poor human souls—"

Martin was kneeling close beside her now, trying to wipe her streaming face with his handkerchief.

"I love you," he said simply. "Come to the land and marry me—that is, if—if—"

She took one of his big bronzed hands and held it against her face, and she spoke very slowly but with a simplicity that matched his own. "I've loved you since first I saw you, Martin. And I saw you long before you saw me—which means I could do you harm, but that was far from my desire. But I must stay below until I have released all the poor souls and broken all the cages. It may take me forever."

"I wish I could help you!"

"No, oh, no," she cried. "You'd be drowned, unless—" She was silent for a moment, thinking. "Unless—unless I could get that old rascal's hat for you, while he is sleeping off a few bottles of brandy from the wrecks. But—I think you had best get yourself a good wife from the land, Martin, and forget all about me."

"Never," he cried passionately, "I—I can't. I never will. Get me the hat."

It was three nights later she came up with the cocked hat.

"Don't let it fall off, my love," she said. "Now—take a deep breath and take my hand. He is asleep and snoring and will be for many hours."

It took them less than an hour to tilt over all the cages and see the little bubbles of souls go up through the water; and another hour for Martin's strong hands to leave every cage a mass of splinters.

"Now," he said, "come." And up they went to the boat. She had a little net bag with her.

"Just some things of my own," she explained. "Unfortunately, no clothes. If I could have a blanket, and then you could go get me a dress or a cloak? This will pay."

She handed him a string of pearls. But, of a sudden, she was weeping again.

"Oh, Martin, your people—what will they think?"

"My people are not given to asking many questions, nor to the bearing of tales. Promise me you'll wait here, or I'll carry you home right now in that fishy-smelling blanket, and in broad daylight. Look, the sun is rising."

"I promise to wait," she said, "and I also promise, as soon as I can learn a bit, to be a good wife to you, and a dutiful daughter to your father and mother, and never, never go back to the sea."

Martin went home on a run and found his mother hanging up clothes. He grabbed a dress from the line.

"Martin, Martin!" screamed Mrs. Grogan. "You're wringing wet! And what are you doing? Have your wits clean left you?"

"No," gasped Martin, "I want the dress for a girl—just out of the sea. You'll take her in, Mother?"

"Oh, the poor lamb!" cried Mrs. Grogan. "Of course I'll take her! Here, take this warm shawl of mine!"

Martin fled, meeting Mrs. O'Connor halfway up the lane. She stared and hastened to Mrs. Grogan.

"I don't know," said Mrs. Grogan, in answer to a volley of questions. "He was in great haste—a girl out of the sea, he said. He didn't say he had saved her, but he was wringing wet. Come in the house, Norah, and kindly put on the kettle, so we can have a sup of tea while I warm some blankets by the fire."

"Ah," said Mrs. O'Connor, with enthusiasm, "that is indeed a fine son you have, rescuing a drowning lass from the murderous waters, likely at the risk of his own dear life. Well I remember his dragging my young Dan from the sea and bringing him home on his back. That was five years ago. This may be some trouble to you, Maggie."

"No, no," said Mrs. Grogan, "it will do my heart good

to have a girl to mother. Sorely have I missed that, with my own two young daughters married and gone to America."

"You should see her," said Mrs. O'Connor, that night, to an ever-increasing audience of interested neighbors. "She is the fairest girl I ever set eyes on and—no, I don't know—I couldn't ask questions with the poor young thing so fresh from the water. She said she came from a far place—maybe she came from a wrecked ship. No. No, not a soul to notify. I gather her family are all gone to their eternal rest.

"But I can tell you one thing—Martin is himself again. He was full of smiles and singing low when he brought in fresh wood for the fires, and he ate a mighty meal of bacon and oaten cakes and honey. And the way he looked at that girl while coaxing her to eat—'twas a sight to see. I'd not be one mite surprised if we hear the wedding bells ringing before long."

And Mrs. O'Connor was right.

THE CORAL COMB

A GROUP of fishermen were gathered around a blazing fire on the shore, awaiting a favorable tide. The dark shapes of their craft lay moored at the water's edge, every net mended and in place, every rope ready. Their pipe smoke rose pungent on the air; their deep voices rose and fell as they reminisced of other fishing times—of that great haul of herring in a long-ago autumn, of the lamentable lack of fish that spring many years back.

"It was the Havrue caused that," said a grizzled old fisherman. "See her, and the fishing will be poor, no doubt of that."

One of the younger men laughed.

"Laugh if you like," said the old man, "but the Havrue is bad luck in more ways than one. Not only a lack of fish but many a storm has she brought, and many a brave man has gone to a cold death in the dark waters."

"Perhaps," said a romantic young lad, "it was not to a cold death he went, but to the Havrue's coral castle below the waves, with the beautiful sea woman for wife, and more fine fish than he could eat in a lifetime."

There was a burst of laughter at this, but a kindly man,

Dirk Larsen, with growing boys of his own, patted the young lad on the back.

"Let them laugh, my son, but 'tis a comforting idea, that. It should hearten many a drowning man as he goes down."

"Well, anyway," said a man who scorned all superstitions, "no one has even reported seeing a Havrue for a good fifteen years—that is, if anyone ever saw one at all. I've always thought those that saw this sea woman were those with poor eyes, mistaking sunshine on a far rock for a gleam of golden hair and the crests of foam on the waves for those white sea cattle she is supposed to herd. But . . ."

"Scoff, man, scoff," broke in the old fisherman again. "But folk have seen the Havrue, my own grandfather among them. And he was a sane and sober man, with eyes keen as a fishhawk's. I tell you that evil sea woman has brought many a sturdy boat to a splintered wreck upon the rocks, and the very stones in our churchyard bear witness to the broken bodies of strong men washed up on the shore—" His voice sank to a whisper, and he pointed a gnarled and trembling forefinger toward the water. "Look! Look, all of you, she has come!"

He stopped speaking and stared. So did all the others.

A little way off stood a woman, so flimsily clad that her slim white body gleamed through the folds of her gown. Her long fair hair hung dripping upon her shoulders, and she was shaking like a leaf in the chill sea wind.

Despite the muttering of his comrades, Dirk Larsen

held out a hand, beckoning her closer to the fire. Timidly she came to sit beside him, wringing out her long hair before the warm blaze and combing it with a little fine comb until it shone like gold in the firelight. But she still shivered and Dirk threw his thick sea jacket around her shaking shoulders.

The fishermen sat silent, all eyes upon the strange woman.

Finally one of them spoke. "The tide is right," he said.

"Ay," said the old man, "but we will catch no fish. And I hope our wives and children and the holy men of the church say prayers for us this night."

They pushed off in their boats, leaving the stranger sitting alone on the sand. When they came back at dawn with empty nets, she was not there. The men in Larsen's boat scowled at him darkly, but said no word.

For a long time Larsen worked around his boat, ever so often gazing out at the sea. He felt a little dazed. Had this night been only a dream?

Slowly he took his way home, to find the young children fretful, for they had hoped for a good breakfast of fresh fish. Karen, his wife, was decidedly waspish.

"You left your jacket on the beach," she said, "but one of your friends saw it and brought it in. You are a careless man, Dirk Larsen. This is a new jacket and not for a year have I had a new Sunday dress. But I am drying it before the kitchen fire and a touch of a hot iron will do the rest. But—no fish. I had hoped for a good haul, for the Christmas season nears and I need some fine flour and a measure

of good raisins and spices for making the holiday cakes."

Larsen felt very weary, and very guilty.

"Today," he said, "I can work on the new boat Thorston is building—he pays well and I will have money by evening."

He worked until darkness fell, and bought the fine flour and raisins and spices and a big piece of ham, and some little sweetmeats for the children as well.

But the homecoming was not as he had hoped. Karen was silent, and the children, watching their mother, were the same. Without a word, almost sullenly, they ate their supper and their sweetmeats and, without protest, went to bed. Then Karen's pent-up anger broke forth. "You were never on the sea last night!" she cried.

He was startled. "Of course I was! I just had poor luck. So did all the others. If you refuse to take my word, ask any of my companions."

"I did. But I take no man's word—menfolk always stand together."

"But, Karen, I don't understand—"

She laid on the table a small comb of carven coral mounted with gold. It glowed and gleamed in the light of the candles.

"I found it in the pocket of your jacket," she said grimly.

He wanted to explain and tried to, though he knew it was well nigh hopeless with so practical a woman as Karen. Often he had heard her speak sharply to the children if they talked of strange folk of the sea.

Well, he had not truly believed in them himself until this last night. And he had almost thought last night had been but a dream. But—there was the comb.

"I will throw the comb back into the sea," he said, "whence it came."

"You will not," said Karen stubbornly. "It is a fine comb. I want it for myself."

"But," he said, "it will be ill luck, indeed, to keep stolen goods."

"It is not stolen. I merely found it in your coat pocket."

"It is neither yours nor mine," he answered. "Karen, I have told you the truth. Please give me the comb."

But she refused, and hid it.

He searched for it each time Karen was out of the house, and at last he found it in a tiny secret drawer in the chest where the best linen was stored. He had forgotten that little drawer was there.

Each time he went fishing he watched for a sight of the Havrue. He would rather give her the comb than just toss it in the sea. When he was not fishing he tramped miles along the shore. His eyes grew strained from the shine on the tumbling waters, and from loss of sleep. His friends noticed the change in him; even his children did. Karen was too busy with her Christmas baking to notice. She had not even missed the little comb.

On the morning of Christmas Eve he and his men went fishing, and it was that day he thought he saw the Havrue on a rock.

"I must swim to that rock!" he shouted suddenly.

His men protested, tried to hold him back. But over the side he went.

"I will be back," he called.

He was a powerful swimmer, but he had misjudged the distance. The tide was against him, the water icy cold. In vain his men strove to get the boat around, but the good wind of the morning had risen to a gale and a fog was closing in. A stout sail tore like thin silk, a strong mast cracked and came down, water poured over the sides. The men, with heavy oars, finally reached the rock. The wind had died, the fog cleared; it was as suddenly still as it had been suddenly stormy.

But Dirk Larsen was gone.

One of the men pointed to the rock. On it lay a small coral comb mounted in gold. They stared at each other and under their ruddy tans their faces were gray and filled with fear. All afternoon they beat around the rock. Drenched and exhausted, they came into the harbor at twilight. The whole town was filled with the warm fragrance of Christmas cooking, the smoke of the new-lit Yule logs rose on the air, every window glowed with the lights of Christmas trees and candles, and from the church came the sweet melody of carols.

But these tired fishermen knew that this night they would neither eat nor sing. Again they looked at each other and there was no need of words. Sadly they reported that Dirk Larsen had fallen overboard. They had done their best, but he was gone.

They made no mention of the little comb. That, for all time, they kept to themselves.

THE NECK

AMONG the strange people of the sea, one of the oddest was the Neck, the musical genius of the waters, of whom tales abounded long ago in the Scandinavian countries. And no two tales agreed on either his personal appearance or his disposition.

He has been reported as an old, old man with a long white beard, as a young boy with golden curls and a red cap. Yet another report insists he is a man to the waist, the lower part of his body that of a horse.

There were those who insisted he only attacked the over-proud and the wicked, but it was a custom to have a bit of steel in one's boat "to bind the Neck" against mischief.

On only one point was there complete agreement, that the Neck could and had taught music to even the least gifted of mortals. His strange price, and naught else would do, was a black lamb and a promise of salvation.

The Neck, at his worst, was no such savage monster as the Nicor, with whom, through the similarity of names, he has been often confused.

The Nicor was a true demon of the sea, a dire menace to boats and unwary swimmers. There was even the terrible rumor that, around his neck, he wore necklaces of the teeth of dead sailors.

My brother saw a Nicor in the northern sea. It was three fathoms long, with the body of a bison-bull, and the head of a cat, the beard of a man, and tusks an ell long, lying down on its breast. It was watching for the fishermen.

—Charles Kingsley, *Hypatia*

THE NECK

ERIC LARSEN had lost count of the times he had asked Thora Lynge to marry him. Not only did she continue to refuse, but she would not give any real reason. His only consolation—and that a poor one—was that, so far, she had not married anyone else.

But this night, so silver with moonlight, so honey-sweet with blossom, he asked her again.

And, again, she shook her head.

"Don't I make money enough?" he asked. "I've enough put by for a neat cottage and all the furnishings, and—"

"That's not the reason," she said. "Eric, ask some other girl. You'll have no trouble at all in getting a wife."

"Do you object to my looks?"

"You are the handsomest man one could ask for! You must know that, with all the girls telling you, and the envy in the eyes of all the young men."

"Then?"

"You'll not like the reason, Eric, but it's this. I'm fond—perhaps overfond—of music. I like someone who can play on some instrument, sing a song, and dance. You can't play anything, and when everyone else is singing you sit closemouthed as a clam. And as for dancing, you are as clumsy as an elephant. Clumsier, no doubt, for I've heard those great beasts are most careful where they put their feet. You can trip over anything and everything!"

Eric looked downcast indeed.

"Even if I could learn to play a bit," he said ruefully, "and I doubt if I could—that wouldn't mean I could sing. And even if I could sing, it would not mean I could dance."

"I think an ear for music," said Thora firmly, "helps all those things. They seem to go together. You're not going home so early?"

"Yes. Early fishing with my father tomorrow. My grandfather is to go with us and he always insists on starting even earlier than does my father. Good night, Thora."

"I am sorry, Eric," she said softly.

But he did not answer.

Eric's grandfather was sitting in the boat before he and his father arrived. As usual, a shining new nail was set in a reed and a knife was stuck in the bottom of the boat.

"Your usual superstitions," said Eric irritably. "That knife is a most handy thing to trip over."

Then he remembered Thora's remark about his ability to trip over anything and everything and fell into deeper gloom.

" 'Binding the Neck' is a time-honored custom," said Eric's grandfather stubbornly. "I don't say the good steel will keep the Neck from drowning us if he so chooses, but I feel more comfortable taking this simple precaution.

What is the matter with you this morning? Thora refuse you again?"

"Yes," said Eric bluntly, "but at last she gave me a reason. I cannot play, sing, or dance."

"Too bad," said his grandfather, cackling with laughter. "That's a fine reason for refusing a strong, steady young man like you. Perhaps the Neck himself could teach you music, but you don't believe in such things."

"Nursery nonsense," muttered Eric. But none the less, he thought about it the day long. And, as they were sailing home, he swallowed his pride and began plying his grandfather with questions.

"Do you really believe in the Neck, Grandfather?"

"I'm not saying. But why else would I insist upon the steel when we go upon the deep waters?"

"Have you ever seen one?"

"No. But I've known those who have."

"Do you think they really teach music?"

"I cannot say, but so I have heard. I knew a man once who said a friend of a friend of his took lessons from a Neck. And, while before that he could get no sound from any instrument save a crash or a squeak and a squeal, and when he sang his voice was as the hooting of owls or the croaking of frogs and his dancing was like that of an ox—afterward no man was his equal at any of these things."

"What does the Neck look like?"

"Reports vary. Why are you asking so many questions? Only a few hours back you condemned the whole matter of the Neck as 'nursery nonsense.' "

Eric spent all his spare time the following month wandering by the water or sitting, hour after hour, on the rocks by the dark fiords. He still did not truly believe in the Neck. But if only—if *only*—he could learn a little music!

Thora spent anxious days and nights when Eric came to see her no more. Perhaps he had now sought out some girl less exacting. Perhaps, also, the music didn't matter. She missed his firm, heavy footstep on the garden path, the sight of his tall, straight figure, his tousled blond hair, his deep-set dark blue eyes.

It was another moonlit night, just about a month after Thora's last refusal, that Eric, sitting disconsolately on a rock by the water's edge, was hailed by a singularly deep and mellow voice.

"Why so downcast, young man?"

For a moment Eric could see nothing. Then, not far from him on the rock he saw a glint of gold—a harp, perhaps?—and a figure, a man with a red cap on wet curls, and the lower part of his body—yes, it was that of a fine gray horse. Eric stared, unbelieving, and rubbed his eyes.

The voice came again. "I was under your boat one day and heard you talking to your grandfather. You did not believe. But—I am the Neck."

He struck the golden harp and played a snatch of melody so strangely, exquisitely sweet that Eric was spellbound; and with it he sang a short song in words Eric could not understand.

"Also"—the Neck spoke again—"I heard, that day, of

the fair girl who refuses you, time after time. There is nothing I so dislike as proud, hard-to-please young women. It does not promise at all well for marriage. You are, doubtless, better off without her."

"Oh, please," cried Eric, "somehow there seems no other maid for me. There never has been, not since we were small children. Do you think you could teach me the music? I have no gift . . ."

"I have never failed," said the Neck, "nor has any of my fellows. You know my price?"

"Yes, sir, I do. The lamb does not seem impossible, though it is seldom they come black. But—but the other—"

"You can try," said the Neck.

And he was gone beneath the waves.

The next morning, a trifle shamefaced, Eric asked his father to spare him from the fishing for a day so that he might go into the back country where the farms lay.

"To look for a black lamb?" said his father, laughing.

"Exactly," said Eric.

Eric's father gazed at him in amazement and alarm.

"I was only joking," he said hastily. "Why, you said—"

"I know," said Eric, turning very red. "But since then I have seen and talked with the Neck. Yes, I am well aware that black lambs are not always easy to find, but—I can look."

He stopped by the priest's before he set forth and unfolded his tale.

"Dear, dear me," said the old man, "what a be-mixture and a misfortune! I fear this love affair has upset your wits a trifle. Now I've known your family for generations and there's nothing in reason I'd not do for you. But—but this! In the first place, I don't believe there is such a thing as the Neck!"

"I have seen him and talked with him," said Eric firmly.

"Very well," said the old priest tolerantly. "But even if I myself saw him I'd not be sure if he were man or beast or evil spirit. I most certainly could not assure him of salvation. Get your black lamb first—and that may not be easy—and then perhaps the Neck will take that and some good coins or such."

So Eric departed, and, with a heavy sigh, the reverend father sat down to his belated breakfast. What a week this had been! Advice asked about stubborn children, on how to get along with unpleasant in-laws, unhappy loves of the young, on emigrating to the fabulous land of America—and now superstition again.

Eight farms Eric visited and at each one every lamb was white as a snowdrift. All the farm folk looked at him a little strangely but all were most kind, offering a bite to eat and to drink.

It was almost without hope that he stopped at a small farm on the way home.

"A black lamb?" said the aged owner. "Yes, I have one—black as soot he is. Oh no, young sir, he is not worth that—just the usual price. It grows late. Will you not share our supper?"

A buxom woman came to the door to echo the invitation. "We can easily make you comfortable for the night," she added.

But Eric refused.

Late next afternoon he took the black lamb to the rock where he had seen the Neck. And the Neck was there. He laid aside his harp, and eagerly, tenderly, took the small lamb. He stroked it, and hung about its neck a string of gleaming pearls.

"And now?" he inquired.

"I don't know," said Eric. "I asked the priest, but he seemed most uncertain. Would you consider taking something else?"

"No," said the Neck stiffly. "Neither gold nor gifts. I have no use for either."

And Eric saw large tears upon his cheeks.

"I'll try again," he cried, and away he went and aroused the old priest from his after-supper doze.

"I have the black lamb, Father. Now you must come!"

Before he was half awake the old priest found himself led down a long strip of beach; and then he was face to face with the Neck, and with the Neck's demands for a promise of salvation at the Last Day.

"I cannot," spluttered the breathless old man, "for I'm not at all sure if you be beast or human. I fear the former, so I've no more belief in your salvation than I have in this dry, ancient staff of mine coming to life. Now, please, Eric, get me home. You are asking too much. I am exhausted."

The Neck hurled down his harp and his sobs fairly shook him. The old priest staggered back along the beach on Eric's strong arm.

Eric felt a real remorse for his own selfishness. He had worn out the good father; he had raised a false hope for the Neck.

He was about to apologize to the priest when the old man stumbled and gasped. "My staff—my staff! Look, Eric, it is putting out a great wealth of green leaves—and fragrant blossoms! It is a miracle! A sign! Take me back to that poor sea creature, my son, take me back!"

A few Sundays later the musician who played the church organ was called away to a sick brother, but the old priest assured every volunteer he already had a substitute for the services. And every member of the congregation was amazed at the playing that day.

Even the solemn hymns seemed to have something in them that had never been there before—the melody of moonlight which had never been truly set to music, the sound of the turning tide which all fishing folk can hear, the change in the wind, the breeze among the pines.

Everyone watched, at the end of the service, to see who came down from the organ loft. It was Eric.

"Oh," said Grandfather Larsen, when people questioned him, "my grandson decided to take a few lessons. No, not from any local teachers, a better master," he said proudly—and also warily. "A good way from here. He takes few pupils."

The next Sunday a new voice was heard in the choir, a deep voice, stirringly beautiful. That, too, was Eric.

Then came the festival of May Eve and Eric sang again, some of the old songs of tradition, some new to all. Admiringly, both the young men and the girls gathered about him, begging him to sing another, and another, and yet another.

But Eric seized one of the prettiest girls and started to dance, light and quick on his feet as a blown feather.

"I didn't remember you as such a dancer," she whispered.

First one girl and then another he danced with, but not with Thora. She had plenty of partners and smiled the evening through, but that night she wept softly into her pillow until dawn.

"Thora," said Mrs. Lynge, after supper the next night, "I promised Mrs. Larsen a taste of these new cookies and the way of making them. Would you take this basket over?"

Thora hesitated. But she was quite sure Eric would be fishing this fine night—unless he were visiting some other girl. She swallowed a lump in her throat and went, meeting Eric just outside his own door.

"Going fishing?" she asked, and then felt very foolish, having seen he had on his very best clothes.

She gave the little basket to Mrs. Larsen but refused to stay.

"I'll walk home with you," said Eric.

"Ah no, don't. Please don't bother. I don't want to delay you from wherever you are going."

"I was planning," said Eric, "to call upon a young lady named Thora Lynge."

"You see," said Thora, as they sat in the garden that night, "I really didn't care if you played or sang or danced. But with so many girls after you, music or not, I—I was afraid. I wanted to see how much trouble you'd take for me. Then I'd be sure you wanted me—and only me—for always."

He tightened a strong arm about her shoulders. "I was always sure, Thora."

She raised her head suddenly, sat straight up, listening. "Eric, do you hear music? It sounds like some of the wonderful things you sang and played! Or is it only the sound of the sea?"

"No," he said. "It is music—played by the master musician who so kindly gave me lessons."

THE FAR HORIZON

LANDS beyond the known horizon have ever held a fascination for all voyagers.

The Greeks had their abode of the dead, the flowery Elysian Fields beyond the dark river Styx. They had also the Gardens of the Hesperides, where, guarded by three fair maidens and the gigantic serpent, Ladon, grew the golden apples of eternal youth.

The Chinese wrote of islands on which grew plants that made men immortal.

There were Avalon, "the Land of Apples" of the Celtic legend, and the Irish Tir nan Og, both lands of perpetual youth. There was the island of Saint Brendan, never found, but occupying an honored, though shifting, position on many an old map throughout centuries.

There was Ultima Thule which was possibly one of the Shetlands or some other tiny island, and the fabulous island of Zipangu, later found to be Japan.

Men made new voyages, new discoveries, but always there was some island over the rim of the sea.

The trustful Columbus, sailing in the West Indies, harkened with childish eagerness to reports of an island peopled with giant apes; of another where dwelt cannibals with the heads of dogs.

Soon after the voyages of Columbus there appeared in Spain a book describing an island called "California." Its location was given vaguely as on the "right hand of the Indies"; its inhabitants were said to be fierce warrior women called Amazons, and beasts called Griffons, half eagle and half lion, who guarded rich hoards of gold and gems. This island eluded the explorers, but gave to the American state its melodious Spanish name.

Like some sea-borne echo from the lands of youth, came the story of an aging soldier of Spain, lured northward by Indian tales of a magic spring whose waters made the old again young.

Juan Ponce de Leon found no spring; and he met death, not the renewal of youth. But he discovered a land so fair, so filled with blossom, it might truly have been Avalon of the legends. This was Florida.

Far to the east of Florida was reported an island with a sinister name and reputation, the "Isle of Devils." Here, wailing storm spirits raced along the shores, and there were forests filled with snarling and dangerous demons. This place was avoided by all seamen until a British vessel, carrying colonists to Virginia in the seventeenth century, was shipwrecked on its dreaded coast. The shrill storm spirits were found to be merely huge flocks of screaming seabirds; the demons only herds of wild pigs.

The "Isle of Devils" has a new name today. It is the serene and sun-drenched winter resort, Bermuda.

THE MAKER OF MAPS

I, BARTHOLOMEW DA ROCA, have found my niche in life, a most important thing to any man. But I spent many years groping to find it. Even had I known my destiny, the fact that I was unlettered would have seemed an insurmountable obstacle in the way of reaching it. Always I have loved line and color, ever rejoicing when the knights and ladies came riding by, for the bravery of color on their costumes and the trappings of their great horses.

And so enchanted I was with the colors in the church that I never slept, as many of the children did, through the long services and the soothing chants.

My parents, I know, puzzled much over me.

"Would you like to be a priest, my son?" asked my father. But I knew I would not.

"It is the color," I admitted, "of the beautiful vestments and of the high windows."

"Color," said my father, thoughtfully. "Well, my brother Pedro was here last week, bemoaning the loss of an apprentice. He does the fine weaving and dyeing of cloth. Perhaps you would like to work for him?"

I thought I would, so to my Uncle Pedro's I went. I liked the dyeing, but I was poor at the weaving and my uncle was not a patient man. And, after all, the fine colorful yards of cloth were but shapeless things, until they were sewn and fitted into garments.

After the long hours with the clacking of looms and my uncle's perpetual clacking of complaints I often sought the shipyard where my older brothers worked as carpenters. There was line here, as well as color—the sweep of the hulls, the rake of the masts, and the coats of arms with their strange devices. I often was allowed to help with the mixing of paints. This, I decided, I would prefer to the weaving and dyeing. But there were, at the moment, enough painters, so I could get but little work. I tried the carpentering but I was poor at that. Then several of the painters left and not only was I allowed to help with the mixing of colors but to paint simple designs. Before long the master painter allowed me to paint a shield with a cross upon it, and then another one with stars, one with three towers, and one with a rose. My brothers were quite proud of me, and more so, when I was entrusted with the painting of three leopards, and then a unicorn. I longed to do an eagle with its elaboration of feathers, and soon was given one. Most of the painters had a tracing to follow, but I was now drawing my designs, that I might

change the curve of a neck or a tail, the placement of a hoof or a paw.

One day the master painter pointed to a fine new vessel that was near completion.

"I wish you to make a scroll for her, of your own designing. The owner is enamored of all these tales of wondrous Cathay, and he desires dragons entwined with the scrollwork. The figurehead will be a Chinese lady—it is being done by a most skillful carver. If—if—you make a success of the scroll, perhaps you can paint the figurehead."

To paint a figurehead! What man could ask for more! I told my family about the scroll but not the figurehead. I might not have that privilege. But the owner was greatly pleased with my scroll and insisted on paying me extra for it. And, of course, I could paint the figurehead. How strange life is! It was that extra pay which changed the course of mine.

It took me into a street I had never entered before, where I was told there was a very fine shop. I wished to buy my mother a little crucifix of real gold, if I had money enough. I found I could buy a beautifully wrought piece and a leather box to hold it. So delighted was I that I took a wrong turn and came upon a very old house with a great window full of wonderful maps. As I stood looking, and wondering into what strange seas my figurehead would go, an old man came to the window, smiled, and beckoned me in.

What a place that was! Maps covered the walls, and on a huge table there was another map, just in outline. Beside it were many quills in a jar, and little dishes of colored inks and paints.

"I saw your interest," said the old man kindly, "and I wondered if, perchance, you were seeking occupation. I am growing old and there are many commissions—every patron demanding a new map as our horizons widen. I sorely need a young apprentice to aid me."

I explained—though, I think, with modesty—about the scroll and the figurehead.

"I see," he said. "Then naturally you would not wish

to come here. I am sorry, for you would be of great assistance, being able to draw and with a knowledge of colors."

"Only a little," I said hastily. "I am only learning." But so eager was I to work in that place that I plunged on. "I am not always working," I said. "I could come sometimes. Oh no, Sire, I would not expect money. I would come as an apprentice only, to help grind the colors, sharpen the quills. My assistance would be very limited, for I cannot—I cannot read or write."

It was the first time I had cared about that—it had never seemed a need in my humble life.

My mother wept with joy over the golden crucifix but chided me for spending so much.

"You should save, my son. Some day there will be a lovely girl."

But I laughed at that notion. I was far too busy to be thinking of girls.

Whenever I was not working at the shipyard, and sometimes after hours, when I was, I worked with old Cabral, the maker of maps. He said I had a real gift for color and line and soon I was helping him with some of the designs on the cartouches and the coats of arms. After we had finished some piece of work he would ask me to stay for a flagon of wine and a bite of cheese with him, and he would explain the maps on the walls to me.

"No, lad, not all of these are mine. Some are my father's and my grandfather's before me. Those early ones of my grandfather's have islands upon them never to this day really discovered. We may conclude that they never existed save in the imagination of man. These islands to the west are believed to be earthly paradises. Here is Avalon, and here is Tir nan Og, the Land of Youth of the Irish. And here is Saint Brendan's Isle, where that long-ago monk found white birds who celebrated the customs of the church as Christians do. Here, in the middle of Asia, is the Kingdom of Prester John, a Christian monarch ruling in the East, surrounded by heathen hordes. And here is Ultima Thule, reported 'nine days' sail north of Britain' and believed to be the end of the world to the north. We know better now. And here is Zipangu, reported by Marco Polo as a city with towers of pure silver and gold.

"As to the Sea of Darkness, no one knew anything at all beyond the Canary Islands. The boats stayed close to the coast, but many of their sailors told strange and dreadful tales about that unknown sea and its denizens—of mammoth whales and monsters of all sorts, including the sea serpent.

"I remember my father telling me of my grandfather's trials. Little was known, but he had some eager and well-paying patrons who wished the terrors of the Sea of Darkness pictured in detail. After all the New World was not yet known, and the Orient was known but imperfectly. To make a handsome map one must fill in some vacant spaces. My grandfather consulted many learned men, but to no avail. Some were skeptical, as was my grandfather himself. Some were merely uncertain.

"So he sought the sailor folk of the western coast in the taverns. They were more than willing to talk, but their stories were seldom in agreement. Only two men had seen —or thought they had—a sea serpent, but all had friends or friends of friends who had. All were ready for argument.

"One insisted the creature had a head like the great crocodile of the East, another that the head was more like that of a large-headed and ferocious horse. Some said the body was scaly, others that it was smooth. There was more contention about a flowing mane. Was it the height of the mast of a ship? Perhaps yes, perhaps no. In their amazement and terror it might only have seemed so.

"And the huge whales—were they the length of an island, the length of a vessel? These sailor folk thought not, but they were in accord on one thing—whales were appallingly large!

"I am glad my grandfather lived to record the voyage of Columbus and then Vasco da Gama's rounding of the perilous cape to find the eastern route to Asia. My father says he was more pleased with that than with the adventure of Columbus, da Gama being our countryman. Portugal might yet be greater than Spain. But a new flag was now unfurled in the New World. Cabot, far north, had claimed a share for England.

"My father's day was almost too full of events. One new map after another. Spain was waxing more and more rich and powerful. She had conquered Mexico and Peru and found treasure incalculable. Balboa fought through a jungle on the Isthmus of Panama, to find, not Asia, but that greatest of seas, the blue Pacific.

"My father was growing old so I made the next map. Spain had laid a new claim northward on the American mainland—Florida. Then Magellan found the winding strait from the east to the Pacific and one of his captains, El Cano, sailed across the Pacific to the Old World. No more arguments now about a round world!

"This map is mine, though my father was yet alive when I made it. Cartier and Verrazano, sailing for France, both found great rivers to the north; and Verrazano found North America very long from south to north.

"My father's words still remain with me. 'Those rivers *may* lead to Asia,' he said, 'but the new continent may well be as wide as it is long or even wider.

" 'And note, my son,' he continued, 'no matter how large this new land may be, there will surely be trouble.

Already too many flags flutter in the wind—rival flags.'

"Here is another map, and well it bears out my father's ideas. De Soto found a mighty river to the west and Coronado reported a vast desert, also westward. This land must be very wide. The French and Spanish fought bitterly for the possession of Florida. And English pirates were attacking the treasure fleets of Spain.

"You," said old Cabral, "may live to know the size and the exact shape of this New World. You may also live to see one nation wane and another grow great. You may see wars."

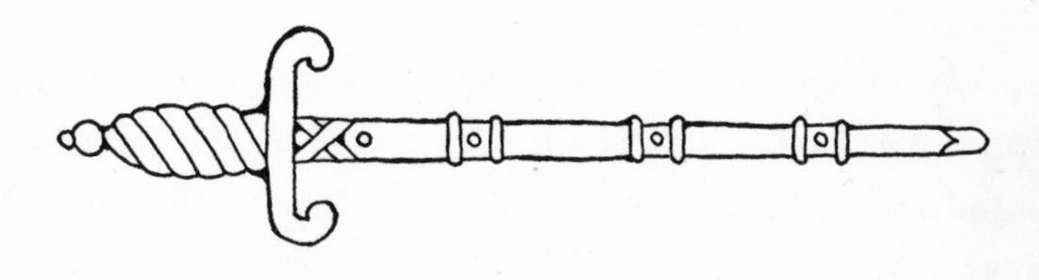

"I wish," old Cabral said to me a few weeks later, "that you could read and write. My old eyes grow more and more weary of the lettering and with your fine hand for a line or a scroll you could easily acquire the graceful sweep of the letters. I have an idea, if it does not displease you. My granddaughter could teach you. We have good servitors, she is unmarried, so she has little to do. It is most unusual for a woman to have the learning, but I taught her some as a young child and the good nuns taught her more."

I did not wholly like the idea of being taught by a woman, but I was eager to learn. I thought I had seen her now and again, entering or leaving the house. A lank woman, she was, with a high nose and stern black eyes. I tried to guess at her age—probably thirty-five or forty.

It was arranged for me to come two evenings a week.

I was picking out letters on the maps when a door opened and old Cabral spoke to me. "Bartholomew—your teacher, Viana Cabral."

So long as life remains I will never forget my first sight

of her. She was slim and small as a child and she had on a dress of old-fashioned cut, green-blue like the sea and like her own eyes; and her hair was black and shone like a bird's wings.

I don't believe I had the wits to say anything, but she

smiled and pointed to a little table with a candle upon it. She was so beautiful in the candlelight I feared I could not even learn the alphabet for looking at her.

But in a short time I had learned it, and she taught me to read, mostly from the old maps, which made it easier. The writing was not too hard, for I liked much to form the shapes of letters.

"You have read everything on the old maps," she announced one evening. "Now you must have books. What would you like to read about?"

"Avalon and Tir nan Og," I said, looking at a very old map.

"There is not much in any one book," she said, after deep thought.

"Tell him yourself," said old Cabral, rousing from a doze. "Let him take notes and write the stories himself—how would that serve as a lesson?"

"Perfect," said Viana. "Thank you, my grandsire."

So I learned of Tir nan Og, the Land of Youth of the Irish where there was ever the sweetness of fine pigs to eat—one ready hot and roasted to welcome a newcomer, another ready to take its place; where there was ever music going and someone to tell a brave tale.

"And," broke in old Cabral, "the ale there, they say, is more intoxicating than that of Erin. And I understand the Irish favor a potent brew. Poor souls, ever hounded by the English, cold, hungry—'tis no wonder the warming ale and the succulence of pigs was to them Paradise."

I learned of Avalon, the Land of Apples, where dwelt

the mighty heroes of an older day—Ogier the Dane, and King Arthur of Britain with his wizard, Merlin, and the enchantress Morgan le Fay, the most beautiful of women. Ogier and Arthur had come there as old and broken men, but in Avalon became young again.

"You are not listening, Bartholomew!" said my young instructress sharply.

But I was. I was wondering what Morgan le Fay looked like, and how Viana would look with apple blossoms in her black hair.

"Lands of youth," said old Cabral, rising. "A happy thought to sleep on—even to die on."

I rose to go also, but the old man put out a hand.

"Do not hasten," he said, "youth is all too brief. It should not be wasted."

I could not see that I was wasting much of mine, what with the ship-painting and mapmaking and now the reading and writing. I was puzzled to know what he meant.

It was some time before I could have any more lessons, for there was a new vessel needing a scroll which I must design at night. There was a figurehead to be painted too, of a girl as slim as Viana and much like her. I sought the owner of the ship, who proved to be a tall, slender man, richly dressed and with slim fingers stiff with many rings.

"If this figurehead is of your wife or a daughter," I ventured, "would you allow me to see the coloring?"

"My wife and my daughters," he replied sourly, "are the shape and size of wine casks, and with swart complexions. Paint this figure as you choose—as the

most lovely woman you have ever seen, my lad."

"And the scroll?"

"Also as you choose."

So I made the scroll of apple blossoms and apples and I painted the figurehead with skin the color of apple bloom and eyes and dress the blue-green of the sea, and black hair.

The owner praised me much and gave me a golden bracelet set with stones the color of sea water.

"For your sweetheart, young man," he said. "For no man could paint a figurehead like that were he not in love."

I suppose I had always known, but had not dared to know.

I went early for my lesson that night and sought out old Cabral. He smiled at me and at my stammering tale of unworthiness, and my fears that Viana would only laugh at me, and so on.

"My old eyes fail me, but I can still see more than you young folk. She saw your figurehead."

"And?" I asked eagerly.

"She wept, as women are wont to do for joy."

Viana uttered a cry of delight over the bracelet when I gave it to her.

"But you should not give it to me," she protested.

"You have been teaching me all these months," I said lamely, "and it is the color of your blue dress."

She rose hastily and went to show the bracelet to her grandfather.

"I will wear it tonight," she said, "but I cannot keep it. You should save it for—for—"

"I have no choice," I said, boldly now. "It was given to me for my sweetheart and for no one else in the wide world."

She looked at me very long and hard.

"You are quite sure, Bartholomew?"

"I am very sure."

She held out her slim arm and I clasped the bracelet upon it.

So you see why, today, I am so contented a man. Old Cabral left me his business and commissions pour in. I have three fine sons to aid me. And my wife, Viana—perhaps she is Morgan le Fay, for Viana is changeless and ageless.

I have just started work on a new map. It is a very handsome map, for it bears many coats of arms: far north that of France; the lion of Britain in that land they call New England, just south of that there is the claim of the Netherlands, on the island of Manhattan; yet farther south is the British lion again, in the country of Virginia. Spain still holds the land of Florida and indefinite spaces of the west.

The ocean once called the Sea of Darkness is a highroad today. Some inland waterway to Asia is still sought, but no man is sure of the width of this strange New World. I hope I may live to know.

FIGUREHEADS

FIGUREHEADS on ships date back to antiquity and passed out of use only with the passing of sailing vessels. They adorned the many-oared galleys of Greece and Rome, sometimes a god or goddess, often some symbol of the cities from which the ships came. The Vikings had carved dragons upon the prows of their ships and the dragons persisted long upon Scandinavian vessels.

Naturally England favored her lion, as did the United States her eagle after the Revolution. Then came many varied devices, depending upon the whims of the owners. Some were reminiscent of classical lore, some were fashioned after designs of the New World.

The great *Sovereign of the Seas* bore as a figurehead the old Roman sea god, Neptune, represented as half man, half fish; the figure on the prow of the *Star of Empire* was a compromise, a goddess of Fame, but wearing on her girdle medallions picturing many of the most popular American statesmen of the day.

The famous *Staghound* bore a gilded stag, suggestive of her speed; the *Westward Ho* of California gold-rush days, the full-length figure of an Indian brave.

The ponderous figure of Daniel Webster adorned the ship of his name; most appropriately, George Washington was chosen for the figurehead of the frigate *President*.

It also became the fashion for the shipowners to name their vessels for their wives and daughters, and even for themselves. But some of these seemingly practical men of business still clung to a measure of romance. So in crowded harbors one would find strangely incongruous neighbors. A vessel with a quaint New England name and a figurehead clad in the sedate costume of the day might be next to *The Mermaid*, bearing a beauteous sea woman clad in nothing at all; or one with such a name as *The Plymouth Rock* alongside such romantically named craft as *The Flying Fish* or *The Unicorn*.

THE FIGUREHEAD

EVERY sailor knows that changing the name of a ship is unlucky, so when a certain young captain, many years gone by, changed not only the name of his ship but the figurehead at her bow, he found it well nigh impossible to gather a crew. The captain had what seemed to him most excellent reasons for the changes, but they were not good enough for the superstitious crew. It is a strange story, and a sad one.

When the captain built his first ship both the name and the figurehead were in honor of his young wife, Eileen Rose, a girl with wide blue eyes and sunny hair. And the carver of the figurehead put her braids around her head like a golden crown and painted her dress blue like the sea at sunset and in her hand he carved a white rose, scarcely whiter than her own little hand itself. It would have been hard, indeed, to find a prouder, happier man than that young captain. A brave ship and a bonny wife —no man could ask for more.

But, within a year, the church bells that had rung so joyously for Eileen Rose's wedding were tolling sadly for her death, and the young captain vowed he would never look at a woman again. And, though the rumor ran that there were a score or more girls who would gladly have married him, he lived alone and lonely for seven long years.

He went to no gatherings, he never stopped in a tavern for so much as a cheery mug of ale, and when he was on his ship he spent overlong hours at the steering wheel and the rest of his time he spent in his cabin. His crew grieved for him, for when the young wife had been alive he had been a man full of laughter and of song and with a friendly word for each and every one of them. Now he seldom spoke.

Then—a very handsome woman came to that port to visit her great-aunt, and very different she looked and seemed from any other of the women in the town. She had skin the color of rich cream, hair black as coal, and eyes to match. Her great-aunt explained that her niece had married a man from Spain and this daughter had taken after the father. Everyone noted that the young captain's eyes followed the beautiful dark woman wherever she went, so there was no surprise when he married her. For a time they seemed very happy; she invited his old friends to the house and plied them with strange, delicious foods and seemed anxious to please him in a thousand little ways. In all save one thing—she would not set foot on his ship. That hurt and perplexed him, for he was proud, indeed, of the *Eileen Rose,* with her gleaming brass and the fine lines of her hull and the great spread of her sails.

And the crew were worried also, for often the wife would come down to the quay, where the men were refitting and loading for a fresh voyage, and she would stand, staring, for a long time, with her black brows knit and her dark eyes full of anger. She never came when the captain was there.

But the cabin boy, who was too young to know better, told the captain, and the captain asked the mate, who was a trusty man and a good friend to boot.

The mate was a blunt man who had never told a lie in his life and he was in no mood to begin now.

"I'm sorry the boy told you," he said slowly, "but it's true. I think she is jealous of the figurehead. Women are made that way. Why don't you ask her?"

The captain was also a blunt man, and he asked his wife that very evening. He was tactful enough not to mention jealousy—he merely asked her why she didn't like his ship.

He was taken aback at the hate in her eyes and the bitterness in her voice when she answered.

"It's that figurehead," said she. "It is most unseemly that your ship should carry the name and the image of a woman long dead. I can scarce hold up my head among your friends, for it means I am merely a woman to keep your house and no more. Your first wife is still in your head and in your heart. If—if you would change the name

—and the figurehead—so that it looked like me—"

"But," said the captain, lamely, "don't you know? To change the name of a ship is most unlucky. My crew wouldn't like it—in fact, they might refuse to sail—"

She was blazing with anger now, and close to weeping.

"Do you think more of your rough-and-tumble crew than you do of me? Must I keep on being shamed? Besides, these superstitions are but old wives' tales."

"Would it make you happy?" he asked, gently, but with a sinking heart.

"Very," she answered, "and proud, indeed."

Her voice and her eyes were soft again, and he looked at her with admiration, thinking what a fine, handsome figurehead she would make. Perhaps, as she said, these superstitions were naught—but—but he had a crew to consider. He slept little and with sun-up he went to see the priest.

The old man thought long before he answered. At last he spoke. "My son—I fear I can help you little in this matter. Perhaps it would have been better had you married a girl of your own land—a—well, perhaps an easier understanding—"

The captain looked at the floor, and he too was slow to speak. Then he raised his eyes to face the old priest squarely. "Ay, Father, ay—I understand what you mean. But one reason I married Carmelita was because she was so different; she could never, never remind me of Eileen Rose."

So great was the sorrow in the captain's eyes that the

old priest had no words. He changed the subject. "As for the superstition, no matter what you or I believe, this may sorely hinder you with your crew. But it is a good thing to have peace and joy in the home. I wish I could help you more—I cannot. Whatever you do I will bless you and your ship, as always."

Slowly the captain took his way to see Belluno, the old carver who did scrolls and figureheads for ships. And as he went he kept going over the priest's words in his mind. As for the superstition, he had not said if it were true, as perhaps a priest would not. He had mentioned trouble with the crew—there was no doubt of that. But he had spoken of peace and happiness in the home—ay, there could be no question of that!

With a heavy heart he entered the great loft where Belluno did his carving. But he put on a bold front; he was even jovial as he told his errand. A figurehead and a fine scroll for the name—

Belluno let his great hammer and chisel fall to the floor with a crash and he was slow in answering. "It is money in my pocket, Captain, but—don't do it. The *Eileen Rose* was ever a lucky ship for you and your good crew. They—they will not like the change."

"Old wives' tales," said the captain.

Belluno shrugged sadly. "You are a young man, Captain, and the young will never take the advice of the old."

"I want it done," said the captain gruffly, making for the door.

"Very well, sir, and I will say the new lady will make a very handsome figurehead. May I have the figure of the *Eileen Rose,* sir?"

The captain wheeled from the door. "Not to sell?"

"Indeed, no, never. But I am growing old; I won't be carving much longer. I have an old man's pride in my work. The *Eileen Rose* is my best. I will set her in my garden where I grow the white roses. I will deduct the price from the new figure—"

"You will deduct nothing, but of course you may have it." The captain laid a bronzed hand on the old man's shoulder and for a long moment he could not speak. Memories were crowding upon him—Eileen Rose sitting in this great loft, that Belluno might look at her the better. And the white roses which had made them think of the rose in her hand. Those, and her own sweet name. "I will come—sometime—to see her in your garden, Belluno," he said at last, "if I may?"

He turned hastily away.

Carmelita seemed very content most of these days, though at times she was sharp.

"Belluno suggested a blue dress," she said with contempt. "I have never worn blue—it does not become me. I want a black dress, touched with gold, and my name in gold, and a red shawl."

The crew watched the figurehead of the *Eileen Rose* cut from the bow and the new figurehead put in its place. They agreed it was a fine piece of work, but they grumbled and muttered among themselves. None of them liked the red shawl and the black dress.

"Red," said the bosun, "is a bad color. It is the color of battle and of blood."

"True enough," murmured another, "but black is worse. It is the color of a pirate's flag—the color of death."

One and all, they refused to sign on.

"What shall I do?" asked the captain desperately of the mate.

"You can do little," said the mate. "But I have one idea. It may be we can talk them into taking you a little way—to some other port where no one will know the story of this ship. Then you can sign on a new crew. I—I am sorry, Captain. I would like to stay with you always, but—"

"Then—you believe—" said the captain, aghast.

"I'm not saying I do or I don't," said the mate, "but my good wife does—and, as you know, there are six children. I can take no chances."

They talked to the crew that night, and they agreed to go as far as a new port—no farther. Only the cabin boy refused, and cabin boys are easy to come by, so eager are youngsters to go to sea.

So they sailed and went to quite a far port. So beautiful was the ship that men crowded the quays to sign on her. And every man of the crew kept silence, as they had promised. Or, if questioned, each had a fine reason for going home—an ailing wife, a bad case of rheumatics, this, that, and the other. And all seemed well.

Until—some of the seamen went into a tavern and whom should they see but their former cabin boy, busily polishing pewter tankards at the bar. He stared at them with round eyes and whispered to the barmaid, who stared also and bustled out. She whispered to the tavern keeper, and he in turn whispered to his fat wife, and she, being a great gossip, did not whisper at all. Down the street she went, like a clucking hen, spreading the news as loud as a hen can cluck.

There were some who paid no heed to this talk but there were others who did, and the captain had to sail a trifle shorthanded. At the next port all seemed well, until a very old man asked if he might touch the beautiful figurehead.

"I was once a ship's carver myself," he said, "but never did I see such beautiful work as this."

When the captain came back that evening he found a knot of seamen awaiting him. Hesitantly, one man stepped forward.

"We are sorry, Captain," he said, "but most of the men are not signing on. You see—well, when the old carver touched the figurehead and the scroll with the name, he said the wood was far newer than the timbers of the ship. So—"

So the captain was forced to sail more shorthanded than before.

Port after port he came to, but wherever he went, some vague rumor of the ship's story seemed to have preceded her. And the captain could hire none but derelict men from the quays, given to laziness and liquor. He found himself steering, unaided, night after night, fearing to give over the wheel. At the last port he himself was so haggard and hollow-eyed that no man wished to sail with him. So with what money he had left he persuaded some sailors to hoist the sails and lift the great anchor. With all sails set and the poop lanterns lit, he sailed, alone, into the darkness.

SUPERSTITIONS

In the middle ages reading and writing were almost unknown even among the nobility, wholly unknown to the peasantry. All matters of learning, even the most simple, were left to the fathers of the church. So, in general, the flocks these patient shepherds tended were a simple people, whose ignorance gave rise to many odd superstitions, some causing fear, others of great comfort.

The clergy were often confronted with these beliefs and some strove to combat them all, but the wiser ones merely tried to separate the harmless from the evil.

If women, as in some places, were comforted by the keeping of black cats which were thought to bring back their sailormen safe from the sea, there was surely no harm in that. Nor was the casting of flowers upon the waves to bring a plenitude of fish a sin, but merely useless.

If, as in the Scandinavian countries, the old habit held of putting a bit of rowan wood into the hull of every boat—well, the pagan origin of the custom was long forgotten, save by certain scholars who knew that the purpose of the rowan was to put a vessel under the protection of the Norse god of storms, Thor. If that bit of wood gave a feeling of safety to the sturdy sailors on the cold, often tempestuous waters, that was well.

The mariners' firm belief that the behavior of birds and beasts gave indications of the weather was, in all likelihood, a guide as good or better than most of the predictions of the day. And even in this modern scientific age such observations prove their worth.

Thus the wisdom of the more tolerant of the holy men of the church has preserved many a time-honored superstition to enrich the lore of the seafaring world.

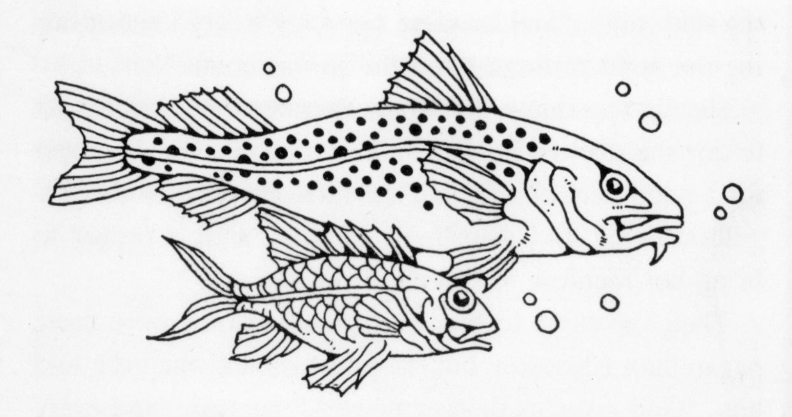

THE LITTLE BOOK

LONG years ago on the coast of Brittany lived a stalwart fisherman, his good wife, and five sons. The fisherman's wife longed for a daughter, but that blessing never came.

" 'Twould be one who would not go upon the water," she said sadly, "and keep me upon my weary knees praying the night through when the storms come."

She did two things that many Breton women were wont to do: she strewed flowers upon the waves, with a prayer for a good haul of fish, and she lifted her eyes to the seagulls mewing and wheeling overhead, with a prayer to bring her menfolk safe home from the sea.

Then she came to fear that these customs were more pagan than Christian, but the priest smiled when she told him. "God gives us the fair flowers," he said, "and every living thing is one of His creatures. It may well be that the flowers and the white birds carry messages to Him in high Heaven."

The words of the wise priest lingered long in her mind,

and when a great storm took the lives of her husband and three of her sons, she remembered them again.

How fine was the profession of a priest—wise, tolerant, comforting. Perhaps—perhaps—one of her sons might become a priest, even a monk in the monastery high upon the cliff. She would see him seldom, but he would be safe.

She spoke of her idea that night. All three of them shook their heads.

"Mother," said Carlion, the eldest, "it takes more than mere willingness to become a man of the church; one must know the Latin and have a memory for the prayers and the conducting of the services."

"And many more things," broke in Peric, the second son. "It is a most learned profession. Besides, how would you live? What scant money we have comes from the fishing."

Guenec, the youngest, said nothing, though he saw the eyes of his brothers and of his mother upon him. But that night, when the cottage was all quiet, he heard her sobbing softly in her room. So, next day, when they were out fishing, he spoke of this matter to his brothers.

"Do you wish to take holy orders?" asked Peric.

"No," said Guenec, "I wish to stay upon the sea, as all of us have done and our father before us."

But Carlion was silent the day long, and, as they came into the harbor at sunset, he spoke slowly, thoughtfully. "Perhaps, my brother, it would be a good thing to become a monk; our mother has worked over-hard for us, and she is no longer young. She has suffered much from the sea. You are fine at the Latin and the reading and writing, as none of the rest of us have been. If—if—well, you could say good prayers for us when the fierce storms come, and, should we go down into deep water, you could say prayers for our souls. And there would be one left to comfort our mother."

Guenec sighed.

"And," went on Carlion, "from that monastery on the cliff you can ever have your eyes upon the splendor of the sea and it is a well-known haven for seamen from all parts of the world—you will learn much."

"Maybe you could write things down," said Peric eagerly. "In a book—knowledge for all sailor folk to come. It would be a greater service than mere hauling on the ropes and dragging the nets."

Guenec was sorrowful and uncertain, but, after a week of thinking and praying, he consented, and so overjoyed was his mother she looked almost young again.

Slowly Guenec climbed the path up the steep cliff and rang the bell by the heavy door in the monastery wall. In the stone arch over the door he noted a carven ship, with a welcome in Latin to mariners of all countries, all beliefs.

An old monk admitted him and led him to the abbot's study. As he went he noticed there were little anchors as well as crosses in the paving stones both outside and inside the monastery. It gave him a strange comfort.

The abbot greeted him warmly and motioned to a

stool. "A few questions, my son. Do you truly wish to become a monk?"

"I—I—I expected to stay upon the sea," Guenec said.

"So did I," said the abbot, "but my mother—" He saw Guenec's face. "It is the same with you?"

"Yes, Father, it is."

"I see. Well, do not take orders yet—first, try it here for a while. But I assure you, you will not be cut off from the sea here. You will hear much sea talk—we have many visitors. I rejoice to have you here; many of my brethren are, as I am, growing old. It will be good to have a young man, fresh from the outside world, to help me welcome our guests."

The abbot found in Guenec a lad both willing and helpful, quick to be on hand when the sea-weary guests came, consulting with the abbot on plans for their comfort, with the cooks about food for hungry men.

"These sailor folk who seek sanctuary here," said the abbot, "are not all of our faith. It is no matter. Many have been long upon the cold waters, often with scarce food enough to keep them alive. Feed them well. Mayhap—mayhap they will notice our abstinence, our observance of fast days; we can but set an example, we must not command."

As for Guenec, he was too busy to be unhappy, and more and more he came to admire, even to love, the tolerant, genial old abbot.

And when the guests came he sat, rapt in attention,

his eyes wide, trying to remember each word these seamen said. He was studying with one monk, gifted in many languages; with another, who had much knowledge of astronomy; and with yet another, to learn to do the fine lettering and illuminations used for manuscripts. Continually, he wrote on scraps of paper. All these things the abbot noted, and made inquiry.

"My brother Peric," said Guenec, flushing, "told me to make a book—a book for the enlightenment of all sailor folk in the future. I do not feel competent, but—"

"It is a worthy idea," said the abbot, "a very worthy idea."

He opened his desk and took out some sheafs of papers, neatly tied. Some were already yellowed with age.

"At your age," said he, "I had the same idea. In fact, I had very wonderful ideas—ambitions. I hoped, some day, to see a book, finely done in black letter, illuminated with handsome capitals, richly bound. I have a fondness for such things, but no gift. Now I am growing old—I have but these scattered pages of notes. A jumble of notes. Take them, if you will, add, change, as new knowledge comes to you. Herein is some of the lore of the ancients, with other things, gathered later. This is the kind of volume which will never be wholly finished—"

Guenec, with trembling hands but sparkling eyes, took the papers.

"Father," he said, "it is an honor, a trust. And I have come to a decision—I wish to—to take orders. If I am acceptable I will do my best."

Guenec's life was a happy one and overbusy. The years went by in what seemed like days. He saw his mother go, but she went with a smile; he saw some of the old monks go, then the abbot. The abbot's last words were deep-graven upon his mind.

"Be ever tolerant, my dear son; keep your heart open, as well as your eyes and ears. The book—"

"The book" were the last words he spoke, and Guenec knew that book had been his great, his lifetime desire. Despite the fact that he himself was now abbot, with added responsibilities, he labored, in every spare moment, upon the old abbot's notes, and plied every seafaring man who came with question after question. More and more he realized the truth of the old abbot's words, "This is the kind of book which will never be finished," but also—remembering the old man's wish for a book richly bound—he finally got enough together for a slim volume, and set a young monk, skilled in leather, to make a binding, and yet another with a gift for working in wood and metal, to make a small box finely polished and hinged with silver to hold the book. All the lettering he did himself.

Then came war, and the monastery was attacked from the sea. Later the enemy expressed remorse, but so stout the buildings appeared, so strategic the position, they had mistaken it for a fortress. But the monastery is gone. Only a heap of stones is left upon the cliff, and in a small museum is the old gateway stone with the carven ship, and what is left of the little book. Many of the pages are gone, some partly burned, torn, crumbled. And on other pages the ink is so faded one can read only a word here and there. But a few fragments remain:

How proud are the men of the Norse countries of their discovery of the New World centuries before Columbus. For they made that perilous journey in open boats and without that later discovery of the compass. There is no real proof that they were there save it is writ in their own sagas, but there is reason to believe. For there are certain red men on the seacoast of America who bury their dead as the Norsemen did, sending them forth upon the waters in their boats which they called canoes, with their weapons with them. And there is a legend among them that one day their god will come over the ocean in the guise of a fair man with hair red-gold like the sun. Such hair many of the Norse folk have today.

It has always seemed impossible to believe some of the old reports upon the size of whales—such reports as ships taking an entire day to sail past one, for example. And though it may be irreverent to doubt the blessed Saint Brendan his statement that he, with his crew, celebrated the Feast of Easter upon the back of one of these monsters, and that it was "the size of a whole country," cannot be wholly believed. Nor that a whale can gulp down a whole ship.

The whaling captain who was here from Spitzbergen assures me that the largest of these creatures ever seen (and he has sailed in many waters in pursuit of them) is near ninety feet and no more.

Under a mistaken idea, many people of our faith have often eaten the flesh of the whale and the grampus, on fast days, thinking them fish. They are not, but animals, bearing their young as do the beasts of the fields.

Also a seaman from the Scilly Isles tells me his countrymen have, over the years, done a most thriving trade in salting the flesh of certain sea birds called puffins, which abound upon their shores.

These they sell as fish—a dire deceit which he has often protested against, but to no avail.

This same seaman narrated a sad saying of the Scilly Isles—that, for every man dying upon the land, the sea will take nine lives more.

It has happened many, many times.

To birds mariners look often. It is said, in the southern waters off Greece and Italy there comes a time—a week before and a week after the autumnal equinox—when the waters are so calm that the beautiful bird, the kingfisher, nests upon the waves and hatches her young.

This time of great calm comes with the rising of the stars, the Hyades, with the sun.

Most certain harbingers of bad weather are those birds called stormy petrels, when they fly so close to the sea they seem to be walking upon the water. Their name, I have learned, is, in Italy, "Petrello," or "Little Peter"—named for the fisherman, Saint Peter, the apostle of our Lord, in memory of that day when he, by a miracle, walked upon the waves of Gennesaret.

I have heard also that many a modern seaman calls these same birds by the odd name of "Mother Carey's chickens." With so many unlettered sailors from so many different ports it is not to be wondered at that the original name suffered this strange change. This name came also from Italy—the petrels were the birds of *Madre Cara,* the dear Mother—the Virgin Mary.

And all men, on all coasts, when they see the gulls flying inland to seek the shelter of harbors, know there are storms to come upon the sea.

As for the widespread superstition that gulls are inhabited by the spirits of dead sailors, that is not . . . [The page is torn here, but it can be concluded the Abbot did not believe, or approve, this legend, for a little further on is another fragment:]

Why should these poor sailormen forever endure the buffeting of the cold wind?

It is a strange thing how the ancients and those after them have seemed to see in the Celestial Heavens some mirror of the waters below: there are both stars and constellations named for creatures of the waves—Hydra, the fabulous nine-headed monster of the marshlands; Capricornus, the sea goat of the zodiac; Pisces, the two fish;

Cetus, the whale; Delphineus, the bounding dolphin; Cancer, the crab.

Even the Milky Way, mostly called by names signifying a road to the Hereafter, has one name relating to the sea.

This was learned by a whaling master who had a native from one of the Pacific Islands on his ship. This dark man was most skilled with the harpoon, but had little of the white man's tongue. But at last the whaling man, having learned a bit of the dark man's language, was able to make out these people's name for the Milky Way: "The long blue cloud-eating shark."

It is a wonderful thing how all seamen, down through the ages, have looked to the stars for guidance. How, even in ancient times, and long since, they have watched for the rising of the seven sister stars with the sun in the spring, and in autumn for their setting. These are the Pleiades, and their rising in the spring means safety to venture forth upon the sea, and their autumn setting, warning to venture no more.

Also, before the compass, seamen had no guide but the stars. The Norse folk chose Arcturus as their guide to the north, naming it the "Northmen's Torch," but most peoples chose the North Star, Polaris. Many a name has this star. The early Anglo-Saxons called it the Ship Star; later it was called the Pilot Star. To the Celts it was the Star of Wisdom or Star of the Sea, and the men of those sea-beaten isles, the Hebrides, gave it its most beautiful name of all, the Home Star.

In the West Indies, so great is the curve of the earth, the North Star cannot be seen, but the Spanish seamen found another beacon set in the velvet dark of the south-

ern sky—no single star but a cluster of stars known as the Southern Cross. And these Spaniards, being of our faith, most reverently gave it yet another name, "The Brooch of the Virgin Mary."

There is much lost of the chapters on the sea folk but a few bits survive:

It is with hesitation we dispute some of the records of the great Columbus—a man brave enough to sail the dreaded Sea of Darkness, without knowledge of where he would find harborage, and with the doubt still existing that the world was round. Many were the prophecies that he might come to the ocean's ending—to a great abyss.

But his report of seeing a mermaid, or sea woman of some sort, must be doubted. There is no such thing. By other seafarers from the West Indies it is reported that there are certain animals, called Dugongs or Manatees, round-headed like humans, which from a great distance could easily be mistaken for women.

Some small superstitions are harmless, such as the custom of a bit of rowan wood set in boats and . . . [The next page is missing.]

As for phantom ships, sailed by strange and evil men, let them be set at naught—these visions can be easily accounted for by fog and clouds and eyes wearied from loss of sleep and long gazing on the tumbling, glassy waters . . .

As for seals who are enchanted mortals and speak with the tongue of men—this is untrue.

It is a known fact that the Norsemen, the Vikings, who raided the northern coasts, were often clad in sealskins, thus leading to this old belief. It is to be admitted that such an idea might occur to unlettered folk, even linger, for when the seals gather upon the great rocks, their cries are strangely human . . . [The following pages are lost.]

For many years, an old, old abbot was wont to come to the little museum. He named a monastery a long distance away. He always asked to look at the little volume, and most tenderly he would touch the old broken stone with the ship graven upon it.

Then, after a time, he came no more.

WIND AND TEMPEST

SUPERSTITIONS about winds and tempests go back far into antiquity.

In China and Japan tumultuous storm clouds were likened to destructive dragons, the shrill screaming of the wind to the ravenous cries of tigers.

Ancient Greece had a god of winds, Aeolus, who kept captive all the winds of Heaven in a bag tied with a silver cord. These he could release at will—even lend them to favored mariners. With the coming of Christianity, Aeolus went the dim way of all the old pagan gods, but over the superstitious followers of the sea he cast a long shadow.

For years Lapland and Finland were reputed to have sorcerers who could control the winds; Druid priestesses sold wind charms on the shores of Gaul; far later an Indian medicine man sold winds on the coast of America; as late as the year 1814 there were reports of a weird old woman in the Orkney Isles who would sell a favorable breeze for a mere sixpence; less than a century ago American sailors, prowling in the ports of China, were offered, by Chinese beggars, excellent winds for sale.

And today, a little shamefaced, often surreptitiously, the modern yachtsman whistles or scratches a polished mast to stir up a good breeze.

SIXPENCE FOR A BREEZE

LYING north of Scotland is a group of little islands called the Orkneys. They are bleak, windswept bits of land, buffeted on one side by the waves of the North Atlantic and on the other by the stormy North Sea. And on one of these little islands, long years ago, lived an old woman, and the word got about through harbors and ships that she would sell a fine favorable breeze for a mere silver sixpence.

There were some seamen who would go there and some who would not. Some reported the breezes were worthless and it was a mere waste of good money; others stoutly contended they had had most excellent luck.

There was a ship refitting there one time, whose captain decided to buy one of those breezes. So he called the mate to him and bade him go to the old woman.

"Don't think," the captain said, a bit shamefaced, "that I hold with this breeze buying, but I think it will please the crew. We've had pretty poor luck of late and they are all downhearted, especially since we lost the cat."

But the mate firmly refused. "I'm not going," he said. "That old woman is a witch—I've heard tell some of those breezes can turn into tempests."

So the captain called several other men, but they had overheard the mate and shook their heads. "Not even if we lose our berths for refusing."

All the crew had stopped work now and gathered to listen, and they sent up a great clamor to have a breeze bought and to find another cat. The ship's cat had not been lost overboard, the worst luck of all, but had merely died of old age or overfeeding, he being an especial pet of the fat cook's.

"Quiet!" roared the captain. "I'd go for the breeze and the cat myself, but you'd all stop working if I turned my back. Now is there any man here—"

A new young man out of Sweden, who had joined the ship at the last port, stepped forward.

"I believe in neither wind charms nor witches," he said, "but, if you can spare me, Captain, I am not afraid to go."

So, gladly, the captain gave him a silver sixpence and a few gold coins to buy a cat.

Again the crew started to yell.

"Get a black cat!" they cried in chorus. "They're lucky!"

"Old Satan," said the cook mournfully, "was black as a coal—not a single white hair upon him."

So the tall young Swede set out, keeping a sharp eye out for a cat as he went. And, as in all seaports, there were many, many cats, for the people treasured them because of the rats which infested the quays. He saw tiger cats and tabby cats, gray cats and yellow cats, even pure white cats, and a few black ones with white bibs and mittens, but no solid black did he see.

He came at last to the old woman's house, and she was old indeed, but spry and pleasant-spoken. She offered a cup of tea while she made up the wind charm, and most gratefully he accepted, for he was somewhat tired and cold, her house being a way out from the town and right on the sea. He could hear the breakers beating on the rocks, and the wind whining just as it did in the rigging of a ship.

"You've not told me where you are bound," she said, "so I don't know what manner of wind you want."

No Scandinavian sailor in those days cared to mention the port he sailed for, that being bad luck indeed. The Swede hesitated. "The captain didn't ask for any special wind," he hedged. "I think any good one will do."

Out she went and soon was back with a cup of tea and fragrant, spicy little cakes and a saucer of milk she set upon the wide hearth. In came a great black cat and started lapping the milk. His fur shone like satin and his eyes were like those gems called emeralds.

"That's a fine cat you have," said the sailor. "All this afternoon I have tried to find a cat for my ship—a black cat with no white hair upon him. I can pay—"

"He has no white hair," said the old woman, "not even those few hairs some black cats have on their chests—but he is not for sale. I'll fix your charm."

The sailor sat drinking his tea and watching the cat. And the cat stared back at him, unwinking, until he was fair uncomfortable before the old woman came back with the charm.

He laid the silver sixpence on the table, and, with it, one of the gold pieces.

"Will that buy the cat?" he asked.

"If I had need of gold, would I charge but a sixpence for a fine charm?" she retorted, very sharp.

He laid another gold piece on the table and jingled the last ones in his pocket. Then he laid another on the table, and the old woman refilled his cup of tea.

"No gold on earth will buy the cat," said she, sharper than before.

But now he was set on the cat, and he kept on.

"We might," said he, with caution, "touch many ports. We—I—could bring you the finest coffee from Arabia—"

"I don't drink it."

"Or sweet wines from France or from Spain—"

"I only drink tea," she said.

"Very well," he promised, "perhaps we could bring you the finest tea from China, and a fine silk shawl embroidered with birds and butterflies and flowers, or one with dragons done in gold thread—or we might—I'm not saying I know—we might touch that new land of Australia and bring you a sack of diamonds—"

That had been a strange, a heady tea. He could hear his own voice ringing in his ears, promising all these treasures, but above his own voice, above the crash of the sea, above the wind, came the old woman's voice, again, keen and clear, and she thumped down a small packet on the table.

"Here's your charm, young sailor, and may luck go with you. Again I tell you, the cat is not for sale—not for silver or gold or anything else. He was born on a ship and when he is ready he will go back to a ship, either for the liking of the ship or some seaman aboard her. I can neither stop him nor urge him."

She opened the door and a chill wind blew from the sea. And a sudden fog had come in. When he looked back he could not see the house. He barely remembered getting back through the town; vaguely he recollected giving the wind charm to the captain and feebly apologizing for his failure to find a cat.

Then, as they told him later, for three days and nights he knew nothing at all, and he spoke no word.

When he did come to, he saw a big black cat on the foot of his bunk. And he would have known that cat among ten thousand cats.

Just then the cabin boy looked in, and the young Swede pointed to the cat. "Where—" he began.

"I don't know," said the cabin boy. "Nobody knows. He just walked on, as the sails were going up, as if—as if he owned the ship. And now I think he does."

A POUND OF TOBACCO

THE INDIAN medicine man dwelt on the eastern shore of America and he would sell three favorable winds for one pound of tobacco. And for nothing else. He would take no coin, large or small, for he had no use for money. Nor would he accept fine cloths, preferring the soft deerhides and furs of his own land, and the proud eagle feathers of his country even to the feathers of birds of paradise or the tails of peacocks—though he was often offered such things by seamen who had no tobacco.

Three winds seemed a reasonable exchange for one pound of tobacco, but it must be the finest tobacco. Men wondered why the Indian was so particular, and, at last, having picked up enough of the white man's tongue, he gave an explanation to a sea captain he had known long and liked well.

"Our people," he explained, "do not smoke as the white men do—no idle puffing on a pipe for no reason save that it pleases them.

"To the red man, smoking is a ceremony and tobacco a plant sacred to religion. The crushed leaves are strewn on the fields before the planting, with a prayer for a good harvest, and scattered from the canoes upon the waters with a prayer for an abundance of fish.

"As for smoking, that is indeed a ritual. No solitary smoking by one man before his own hearthfire; it is at councils held around the tribal fire that the great pipe, the Calumet, carefully carved and decorated with the finest of eagle feathers, is lit by the chief. And each puff of smoke has a reason and a meaning.

"The first puff is upward to the sky and to the sun, the symbol of the Great Spirit. Then three puffs to the three elements, to the Earth, which gives us food and firewood, to Water, which quenches our thirst and gives us fish, and to Fire which warms us and gives us light in the darkness.

"Then the Calumet is passed from hand to hand around the council fire and if a man refuses it he is in disagreement with the rest.

"There might be, around that fire, men of the same tribe, bent upon some grave decision. There might be men of other tribes, with pacts to be made of war or of peace. There might be men from the white-sailed ships, like yourself, with treaties to be made.

"If the Calumet is accepted it is a sign of agreement—a promise of peace.

"So you see," ended the medicine man, "why the tobacco must be good. Its fragrance must be welcome to the Great Spirit, and, also, would any wish to give poor tobacco to a possible enemy?—and certainly not to a good friend!"

UNLUCKY PASSENGERS

WHILE many of the superstitions of seafaring men are so old that their origins are forgotten, belief in some of them is still as strongly rooted as ever.

Many a modern shipping magnate has been puzzled by the difficulties of getting a crew. The first thought is wages—are they not adequate? How about the food? The quarters? The real cause is probably the last thing thought of, if it occurs to the owner at all. Possibly the captains, if they chose, could give some enlightenment, but, sitting in these modern offices, it seems somewhat incongruous to speak of strange beliefs.

Certain people aboard ship, since the days of the unfortunate Jonah, and doubtless long before, have been considered unlucky. In sailing days a Russian Finn was scowled upon by his shipmates. Even on a modern liner one may hear that a member of the clergy is likely to bring poor luck and that nuns cause stormy weather.

After all, sailormen are a race apart, and superstitions cling to the seafaring world even as barnacles cling to the weathered hulls of ancient ships.

THE VOYAGE OF *THE LASS OF GLASGOW*

CAPTAIN ANGUS McMANUS, of the ship *The Lass of Glasgow,* sat comfortably in the offices of the shipping firm of Dunbar and Gordon, bent over a pile of sea charts. Mr. Dunbar and Mr. Gordon were also absorbed in piles of papers. By the window sat the mate, the captain's nephew, Donald McManus, busy with a stack of cargo lists.

Captain McManus was a stern man, with occasional bursts of temper, but he was not an unkind one—he was noted for fair treatment and supplying good food. It was never difficult for him to get a good crew. Many of his seamen had been with him for years.

"It is not an economy to underfeed your men," he would often say, as if in apology for a seeming lack of Scotch thrift. "On good food they work better and quarrel less."

"True, true," assented Mr. Gordon.

"Have you a good crew for this voyage?" asked Mr. Dunbar.

"I believe so. My trusty men, as usual, and a few extras —this will be a long trip. I have a couple of fine, stalwart Negroes, recommended as sailors, who will be able to give us some assistance as we near their native coast of Africa, a few Spaniards, Japanese, and Chinese who can do the same—also act as interpreters, if need be. A mixed crew, yes, but if they are all of the same country they invariably get into political arguments. If some are from other places—we-eel, they are more likely to exchange tales of their native lands, bragging a bit, of course—a harmless pastime." He laughed. "Of course I will have the usual trouble with superstitions, but, as usual, I will make a short talk on that matter before sailing. These superstitions are trivial but can be a nuisance."

"Of course, of course," said Mr. Dunbar.

"Yes, of course," agreed Mr. Gordon.

"Captain"—they spoke suddenly, in duet—"won't you have dinner with us?"

"Thank you, no. Most kind of you both, but I'll get a quick bite at the tavern. I have a few last-minute things to do."

He was vaguely aware that the owners had something on their minds. They had risen to leave, then sat down again. He saw them exchange glances.

"Captain," said Mr. Dunbar, with hesitation, "would it be possible for you to carry three passengers?"

"I have never carried passengers," said Captain McManus bluntly. "I am not equipped for it."

"These passengers," broke in Mr. Dunbar, "would not expect luxury, sir. Where they are going they will not even have comfort. They are bent upon holy missions, and we have had requests from people in high places, and—in a roundabout way—this might, we believe, open up an avenue of—er—profitable trade for your assorted cargo, not only on this voyage, but—"

"Who are the passengers?" asked Captain McManus suspiciously.

"Well," said Mr. Gordon, "an archbishop requested we arrange passage for the two women, and he is most eager for the finest ivory for a statue of the Virgin. The other gentleman is very high in his church and a most godly man—there is no connection, naturally—"

"Who are the passengers?" the captain demanded, losing patience.

"A clergyman of the Presbyterians—he is bound for a mission—and two nuns for a newly founded hospital for the benighted Negroes. They only wish to go to Africa—"

"I don't like the idea at all," said Captain McManus irritably, "but, if you insist, I will think it over. I will let you know this afternoon."

Solemnly Mr. Dunbar and Mr. Gordon took their way to dinner and barely had the door closed when young Donald McManus was on his feet.

"Uncle Angus, you can't do it—you can't—holy missions or not! And you can't tell me the firm of Dunbar

and Gordon is not getting a profit out of this. They might have spoken for a minister of their own faith, but Catholic nuns, with both of them so anti-Popish—"

"Hold your brash tongue, Donald!" shouted the captain. "Don't come telling me my business. I was dealing with Dunbar and Gordon while you were still a bawling bairn in the cradle. They have ever dealt honestly with me—"

"But they are not above making an extra penny on the side. Besides—"

"Besides, what?"

"Of all things! A clergyman and nuns! You'll have a fine time with your crew, Uncle Angus—you'll find few of them who don't think a clergyman ill luck and that nuns bring stormy weather!"

"Merciful Providence!" roared Captain McManus. "Are we to begin on these idiotic superstitions even before the anchor is hoisted from the mud? I thought you had outgrown such notions! When I first took you on as a cabin boy you had an obsession, picked up somewhere, that a shark following a vessel meant he was after someone on board—preferably you—though what self-respecting shark would have looked at your lanky body at that time I can't imagine! I explained to you that sharks often follow a ship, hoping for a tidbit thrown from the galley. I truly thought—hoped—you had outgrown such childish—"

"I think I have," retorted Donald hotly. "That does not mean your crew have. Here come the honorable firm of Dunbar and Gordon—and, I believe, the clergyman. I am going over to the warehouse."

Captain McManus loved his orphaned nephew as if he were his own son. But there were times when he found young Donald's advice difficult to bear. These absurd remarks of Donald's had decided him in favor of the passengers. He nodded a silent assent when Mr. Dunbar ceremoniously introduced the minister, Mr. McLeod.

The captain took an immediate dislike to him. He was quite stout, which the captain, somewhat unreasonably, deemed unseemly in a man of the cloth. And his efforts at cordiality seemed a definite effort.

"I am most grateful to you, Captain McManus, and the good sisters, I am sure, would wish me to express their thanks with mine. They are of a different faith from yours or mine, but one must be broadminded. Their mission is dedicated to the welfare of human beings, as is my own—"

"How much luggage have you?" asked the captain abruptly.

"Very little—my scant clothing and a small box of Bibles and hymnals—and the holy sisters have little, save a small chest of medicaments. Oh, by the by, the sisters asked if they could have their meals served in their cabin. You have a most bonny ship, Captain, if I may say so."

"The luggage had best be put on board this afternoon," said the captain, with a brief nod to Mr. Dunbar and Mr. Gordon. "I leave that to you, gentlemen. Our business seems to be complete."

He strode over to the tavern, where he found Donald.

"I thought," snapped the captain, "you were at the warehouse."

"I was—everything is now in order. This noon you were so busy berating me neither of us got a bite to eat. Sit down, Uncle Angus, you must be hungry."

"I believe I am," said Captain McManus. "I forgot food with this fresh problem of passengers on my mind. Yes, that was the Reverend Mr. McLeod. I suppose he will have to eat with us—the nuns will not. Well, they will only be with us to Africa. I foresee no undue trouble."

Donald kept his eyes discreetly on his plate.

As the captain strode up the gangplank next morning his way was blocked by two of the Spaniards, arguing so heatedly they were wholly oblivious of his presence.

"I would like to be able to board my own ship," he said loudly.

They jumped and hastily backed against the ropes. The older one apologized. "I am sorry, Señor Captain. My brother here is lefthanded and it often mixes him with his feet. You see, in our country, it is most evil luck to step aboard save with the right foot first."

"I see," said the captain grimly.

At the sound of his voice the bosun and some of his men came running.

"We didn't expect you so soon," gasped the bosun. "We were all on the far side watching them raise yon ship. I'd never sail on her," he added.

"Why not? 'Tis a good ship—merely needs some few repairs."

"Because, sir, come nightfall that vessel will be filled with the woeful cries of all the poor souls who went down in her—"

The captain snorted and made for his cabin. "Send the mate to me," he ordered sharply.

"Come in and shut the door," commanded the captain when Donald appeared.

"Already I have listened to two idiotic superstitions," said he crossly. "I want all the men gathered on the deck. I wish to speak of these matters before sailing. How did the crew take to the idea of the passengers?"

Donald hesitated. "Not too well," he said, which was decidedly an understatement.

The crew stood, attentive and respectful, caps in hands, for the captain's speech.

"Now, my good men," said the captain, "I see you have the ship in most excellent shape. But, before we sail, there is one matter I wish made clear. That is the subject of ridiculous superstitions. You disturb yourselves with this nonsense, also your crew mates. I wish no reports that this staunch ship is about to sink because a rat falls or is chased overboard by the cat. I wish no good loaves of bread thrown into the water to please Saint Nicholas, every time the breezes stiffen, and most certainly no ale poured in the waters as an offering to some pagan seagod. I wish no alarming tales of ghostly ships which turn out to be clouds, no mythical islands reported—which do not exist, as I know from my charts, and they are good charts. There are many more of these notions, but this is enough, I believe, to make my meaning clear. I hope," he ended genially, "that this will be a fine voyage, and a profitable one for all of us."

Captain McManus sat down to supper with relish—not only was he very hungry, but this was an excellent opportunity to study some of the new members of his crew. The ship was going at a good even rate. Most courteously, he invited the Reverend Mr. McLeod to sit on his right. He was in high good humor, but it did not last.

"Why do you turn your plate so carefully?" he asked a new officer from Cornwall.

The young man flushed painfully. "Sir, in my country

we always eat our fish that way—head inward, tail outward—to bring more fish to our shores."

"What a quaint custom—delightful," said the Reverend Mr. McLeod. He shifted his plate.

"Do you suppose a fish knows its head from its tail?" barked the captain.

"Ach, ach, ach!" muttered the third mate—a tow-headed young Hollander. "I am so sorry, Captain—I have spilled the salt!"

"Accidents will happen," said the captain kindly.

"But, Captain, sir—it means the wreck of a ship—"

"Well, well," said the Reverend Mr. McLeod, "I am a landsman, I did not know of these—er—charming little beliefs. I must write some down."

"Stuff and nonsense," said Captain McManus. "The Hollanders are a thrifty people—as thrifty as the Scotch. They don't want salt or anything else spilled."

He saw Donald eying him, his mouth sober, his eyes dancing with mirth.

The days went swiftly, with the sea calm but the good winds continuing. Table talk was a little strained. The Reverend Mr. McLeod told, at length, of his proposed mission to Africa; the young officers listened politely; the Captain often excused himself to take the wheel or to study his charts. With the weather so temperate, the winds so favorable, the captain concluded that the crew had lost their fears of the passengers.

Donald knew better.

The first storm came when they were nearing Africa; a second one followed, then a third, more violent than the others. Everyone snatched a bite when he could—Mr. McLeod was absent from the table.

The ship rolled, pitched; there was a constant sound of splintering spars, tearing sails, running feet. The captain was at the wheel day after day, night after night. The seventh night Donald insisted that he get some sleep. But at dawn he burst into his uncle's cabin without even knocking.

"We are almost on an island—or a reef or a rock!" he yelled above the tumult of the storm. "I don't know who reported it—"

The captain consulted his charts, under the swaying lamp. "There is no island on my charts—no reefs—no rocks—"

The ship struck with a resounding crash. The lantern fell and went out, the pile of charts slid to the floor, the ship shuddered and lay still.

"The crew have been wonderful, Uncle Angus, but last night they were beginning to get out of hand. I almost had to wake you. They do not like the passengers. I told you—"

Amid a welter of torn sails, broken ropes, and wood, the crew staggered to attention as best they could on the slanting deck, as the captain came on deck. All of them looked very wan in the gray light of dawn.

The ship's doctor came up, escorting the nuns, almost

as white as their wimples. The Reverend Mr. McLeod appeared, somewhat pale and shaky.

"Well," he said, "a shipwreck. An unfortunate but interesting experience—one to be borne with fortitude. Life has its ups and—"

The head of the bosun appeared from a hatch.

"Hole torn in the bow, sir; water is coming in," he announced briefly.

"Man two boats," said the captain, with equal brevity. "Take the passengers and some provisions ashore."

Tirelessly the captain himself saw to the mending of the leak, the pumping out of water. At the end of a week the ship was lighter, righting herself.

"If we could only get off this wretched reef," said Captain McManus, "we could make our port in three days. Don't use that plank, Mac—get a heavier one. Well?"

One of the huge Negroes was waiting. Donald was just behind him. The Negro burst into speech.

"I don't understand you," the captain interrupted. "Speak English."

"He is speaking English," broke in Donald. "The Reverend has been prowling all over the island, picking plants, some poisonous. This man does not consider it safe. He says there are venomous vipers, cobras, crocodiles, possibly cats—"

"Cats?"

"Oh, not fireside cats," explained Donald patiently. "Big cats—lions and such."

"I've no time to be concerned with crocodiles, cobras, or anything else. Tell that Reverend to stay on the beach. Make that pitch a mite heavier, Jock—"

"This is your first disaster, Captain," said the bosun mournfully. "Shame to break so fine a record. I could wish we had never took on the passengers."

"The passengers have nothing to do with it—get that out of your mind," said the captain, gruffly. "Anyone can have an accident. The ship is lifting more—here, some of you men, shift some of the cargo to the port side."

The captain went on deck at dusk. One of the Negroes came shyly up to him, pointing to the sky, to a thin moon.

"There will be a great tide tonight, Captain. It will float the ship from the reef."

"She is beginning to float now!" cried the captain suddenly. "Run, boy, get the mate for me!"

Donald came running.

"Get the passengers on board," the captain ordered. "The ship is off the reef!"

In three days they knew they were nearing their port. More and more huge canoes hailed them; soon they saw crude quays jutting out into the water, clusters of palm-patched huts, a few white buildings, long lines of men laden with ivory tusks, coming from the forest to the waterside.

There were a priest to meet the nuns and several men to meet the Reverend Mr. McLeod. They looked incongruous in their somber clothes and white topis.

Thanks were showered upon the captain; he received

them somewhat grimly. Before all the ivory was loaded the passengers and their escorts had disappeared into the blackness of the jungle.

"Listen!" said Donald, at the Captain's elbow. "Our crew are singing again! It is the first time since we left Glasgow!"

Captain McManus and Donald sat once more in the offices of Dunbar and Gordon. It was almost as if they had never been away.

"A magnificent cargo," said Mr. Dunbar.

"Magnificent," echoed Mr. Gordon.

"We have many orders already in," said Mr. Dunbar.

"Your percentage on the orders?" inquired the captain.

Mr. Dunbar fidgeted uneasily. "Oh, well—a mere pittance," he replied. "Of course there were a few little expenses necessary to negotiate these—"

"Make out your percentage," said the captain, feeling Donald's eyes upon him.

"Did you have much trouble with the superstitions?" asked Mr. Gordon, hastily changing the subject.

"Some," said the Captain, rising to go. "In fact, more than usual. But I am now convinced that I should be more tolerant on these matters. Yes, Mr. Dunbar, we sail again in two weeks. And, gentlemen"—he paused at the door—"we will carry no passengers."

TERRORS OF THE SEA

ADDED to the natural fears of storm and fog, dangerous coasts, and uncharted seas, the early mariners had others far more appalling. In those days of ignorance and superstition, the blundering sea beasts became dread fiends of evil, the roar of water against rocky cliffs the bellowing of monsters in anger.

To the ancients there dwelt on the Italian side of the Strait of Messina that terrible creature Scylla, with her ghastly heads set on snaky, far-reaching necks. Opposite her, on the coast of Sicily, lurked Charybdis, who spouted huge columns of water, in which whole fleets had been engulfed. Calmer coasts were made perilous by the sirens, whose exquisite singing drew many a vessel into treacherous waters.

With the passing of the years men learned that Scylla, with her crushing fangs, was but a jagged rock, Charybdis a deep whirlpool, the songs of the sirens the murmur of waves over dangerous reef and shoal.

But new and longer voyages brought new tales of terror. From the seas around England and Norway came reports of the Kraken, a sea devil with many long and almost endless arms, which could reach to the topmost masts of vessels and drag them down into the depths. The Kraken proved to be the giant octopus—truly a menace to unwary swimmers and small boats, but hardly to large craft.

Another place of terror was that fearful sea strewn with rotting hulks where the skeletons of the crews were held captive forever by a myriad of clutching hands—the drifting weeds of Sargasso Sea.

And there was the sea serpent. It was pictured on many an old map, towering and immense. Its existence has been much questioned, never wholly disproved. The fact remains that some such creature has been reported throughout centuries, and with considerable, if varying, detail. The sea serpent seems destined to be the sea's last mystery.

THE SEA SERPENT

IN THE snug taproom of the Silver Anchor sat Captain Conrad Barry of the ship *Cormorant* and his mate of many years standing, Jerome Foyle.

"All crews are mixed, bad and good," announced Mr. Foyle, "but this one seems fair to middlin'. All but that young second mate you signed on—I think little of him."

"Well recommended," said Captain Barry, pushing some papers across the table. "And, before you can ask me, he did not lose his last berth. He sought a new ship with a new route of his own accord. He is studying at a university and his graduation paper is to be on marine life. He especially wishes to disprove the existence of the sea serpent. That is, he is sure he can place it as—what did he say—oh, yes, a rare form of some other known species, seldom seen. He used a number of scientific names, but those I forget."

Mr. Foyle gave a sudden snort and slammed the papers on the table. "Cedric Noel Sandringham-Smythe!" he roared. "A handy name to call in a storm! And well I know how these Britishers cling to their double names! Think they're stylish or something. Well, he'll be Mister Smith to me and that's that!"

"Now, Jerry, don't be unreasonable," protested Captain Barry. "Education is not a sin."

"And no good, neither, not on the sea," retorted Mr. Foyle. "Marine life! I know a shark when I see one and a good edible fish from one poor for the stomach! As for sea serpents, more than one honest, sober seafaring man has seen one-and they all agree they ain't like any other animal on this earth—"

Mr. Sandringham-Smythe entered at this moment, bowed politely, took a distant table and ordered tea and toast, without butter. Mr. Foyle glared.

"Have another drop of ale, Jerry," suggested Captain Barry. "It might make you feel better. I'll have one with you—we have much to do tonight. Emma Kate, will you refill—"

"I'll take whisky and water," Mr. Foyle interrupted, "and you can measure the water in a teaspoon."

"Well, Jerry," inquired Captain Barry, after some weeks, "how is the second doing?"

"Not bad," said Mr. Foyle grudgingly. "Attends to his

duties very prompt; neat, alert—though how he can be that I don't see, for night after night I see a light in his cabin at all hours—readin' and writin', I take it. The crew don't like him."

"Any trouble?"

"Nothin' to speak of, save with the cabin boys. One of 'em threw out a bunch of shells and stuff he's been collectin' on the beaches—the boy said the place smelt like a fish dock. Mr. Smith was in a real takin' over that. 'Invaluable specimens gone,' he says. Now he insists on cleaning his own cabin."

"Well," said Captain Barry, "as long as the smell doesn't bother anyone else, we'll let the matter go for a while."

Captain Barry was aroused from sleep by shouts and running footsteps, the flap of sails and whine of ropes, the lowering of boats. He hastened on deck.

"Mr. Smith," roared the bosun, "has disappeared!"

"Overboard?"

"Don't know, sir, but he's nowheres about. One of the men—Rafferty it was—was goin' off duty and he saw Mr. Smith a-leaning over the rail and a-talking to himself. Rafferty got a cup of coffee in the galley—a matter of minutes—come up for a breath of air before turning in, and Mr. Smith wasn't there. He thought likely Mr. Smith had gone to his cabin, but somethin'—Rafferty don't know what—made him go below to see."

"No one heard a splash?"

"No, sir, but you see, the wind was rising some and the waves slapping at the hull—we are in for a blow."

The boats searched far and wide until long after dawn, but with no sight of "Mr. Smith."

"Mr. Foyle," said Captain Barry formally, "I think we had better take a look at those papers we saw on the second's table. Whew! It does smell in here. We'll take the papers up to my cabin. Come along."

"I ain't interested in marine life," growled Mr. Foyle.

"That's beside the point," said Captain Barry firmly. "I want you with me when I read this document."

"Yes, sir, as you say."

The document found in Cecil Noel Sandringham-Smythe's cabin was strange indeed. It read as follows:

I shall be obliged to change the subject of my University thesis entirely. For the most unexpected experience has come to me. I have seen the sea serpent and he is not, as I, in my ignorance supposed, allied to some other known species. He stands alone—unique. I say I have seen him; moreover, I have talked with him—a most interesting personage.

It came about this way—I will endeavor to set all down just as it occurred.

FIRST NIGHT

After my watch I found my cabin quite stifling so came on deck again. There was little breeze. We were going very slowly, at times almost standing still. And the sea was so glassily calm I was surprised to see a sudden long ripple on the water, close to the vessel's side. Then, as I watched, a head came up, and up, and up—a huge head on a long snakelike neck. The creature gazed steadily at me with pale, glittering blue eyes. I was frozen with fear—I could not call to my companions. I don't know why, but when I could get my voice at all I said, "Good evening."

"Good evening," the creature replied politely.

I must say his speaking didn't make me feel any better, but I managed to stammer the start of a question. "You are—"

"Yes," said he, raising his head still higher and looking very proud. "I AM the SEA SERPENT! And I don't belong to any of the marine species in which scientists have striven to catalogue me. I am ME, myself, and I and my family before me have been sovereigns of all the Seven Seas since time began. What time is it?"

"Eight bells, Your Majesty."

"Oh, never mind fleeting snatches of time like that. Never mind the day, or even the month. We are so long-lived a family we count only years, and not always those —sometimes just decades. And don't bother with 'Your Majesty'; 'sir' will do."

"Yes, sir," I replied. "It is the year Eighteen-forty-two."

"That makes me about three hundred years old," the creature remarked.

"May I ask, sir, where you live?"

"Well, I cruise a good deal," said he, "but when I

choose to rest up—say, in stormy winter weather—I've a fine palace at the bottom of the sea. Atlantis, it is called. 'Lost Atlantis,' I believe it is known as by mankind."

Now I had heard often of Lost Atlantis, and I knew also how many a sailor, leaning over the bulwarks of his ship, has thought he saw, beneath the blinding shimmer of shifting waves, the dim pattern of a city—the outlines of long ramparts and tall towers, the tangled loveliness of ancient gardens; has thought he heard, above the sea wash, the faint ringing of melodious bells. But I had thought this only an illusion, created by a few sunken rocks, waving seaweed.

I said as much to the sea serpent, but he shook his massive head. "No illusion at all. It's there, and very beautiful it is, only the people are gone. When the sea rolled over that city many were drowned, but a few survived. Long before my time, of course, but one of our remote ancestors saw that great flood and saw the poor people trying to swim and clinging to scraps of old wrecks. Only a few got to land and those to the Americas."

"Then you believe the American Indians are the survivors of Lost Atlantis? I know it is a theory."

"It is the truth. They are wholly unlike any other people in the world, are they not? And I can tell you another thing. You, being a scholar, must know how great a difference there was between the Indians of South and North America before the white men came plundering. It was this way. Some of the older people of Atlantis got through the calmer southern seas to South America and they remembered all the ways of civilization and started straightway to building palaces and temples, and weaving and dyeing cloth to make garments for themselves, and fashioning gardens with the plants they found on the new land, and making jewelry as befitted their station in life.

"But it was mostly the very young who got through the stormy and colder waters to North America, and they knew little and quickly forgot that. So they built no temples or palaces, they dressed in the skins of wild animals, and they only planted a few simple things to eat, and they went wandering about, so there was never a city built at all."

"Most interesting, sir," I said, "and a most reasonable explanation. And now, if you don't mind, would you tell me about the Lost Land of Lyonnesse?"

"To be sure. My grandfather and father kept that—better climate for old age. Not all of Lyonnesse went under the waters. The remains are the Scilly Isles, tiny islands off that southern tip of England they call Land's End, and strangely enough, while England still shivers in her foggy, wet winters, the Scilly Islands get an early, early spring, with a multitude of blossoms and singing birds soaring up from the South.

"And if you are ever there you'll see huge, broken columns of stone older than known history. They are set in great circles as if they once supported roofs of palaces and temples. But who worshiped there or ruled there nobody knows. The rest is in the sea, a fine palace—Someone is calling you."

I was full of a thousand questions. I asked to see him again.

He nodded. "We old folk like to talk," he said, and he seemed to be smiling.

Though I must say when he opened his mouth it was a fearsome sight to see.

SECOND NIGHT

It seemed to me my watch would never end that night and I kept thinking of more and more questions and wondering which to ask first. If—if he came.

He did, as he had promised.

"Well, young man?"

"Sir, if you don't mind, I'd like to know about the old gods of the sea."

"To be sure. Well, I'd be hard put to say if they ever existed at all save in the minds of men, but then it's also possible they did, but fled when all the church bells started ringing for the new Christian religion. For I've understood the pagan folk, from god to small elf, were in fear of the sound of church bells.

"As for myself and my family, we never saw any of these gods. I can only give you my personal opinion, no more. Greece and Rome, with their Poseidon and Neptune, and their fine chariots drawn over the waves by fine horses and attended by tritons blowing on trumpets of conch shells, and the sea nymphs, and the fine flocks of cattle—now, my opinion is that those chariots were but a long line of crested waves and the plunging horses but sportive dolphins, and the fanfare of trumpets but the roar of the sea. And the mermaids with their white bodies —only sea foam and their long hair but floating seaweed.

"Most of the countries had similar ideas. The Scandinavians, for instance, with their god, Aegir, who could stir the sea to tempests at will, so that his wife, Ran, evidently a most grasping woman, could get treasure from the wrecks, and their Odin, riding a gray horse upon the waters—mist and fog, I'd say, nothing else.

"And there was Ireland, with her Manannan, sometimes friendly, sometimes hostile—merely a change in the weather. Ireland had also a sea god, Lir, whose children were all reported to be turned into swans. Swans are a most natural thing—no reason to believe aught else.

"The same would be true of ancient India, whose people claimed that their god, Vishnu, often appeared as a fish or half a fish. They likely saw a fish—no more. And there are plenty of fish in the sea.

"About that old saying for death at sea, 'Going to Davy Jones's locker,' that is a hard question. Some think that the name Davy came from India—from one of their gods, Deva—and Jones from the unfortunate Jonah in the Bible, but in the older days, most folk thought the idea of Davy Jones came from that wicked old Scandinavian god, Sjonji. Names often get mixed among all these seamen from different lands. Anyway, Sjonji was reported most wicked and vengeful; if he could wreck a vessel, he did.

"Even in my lifetime, in those islands called the

Hebrides, the people, though long converted to the Christian faith, on All Hallows' Eve, would still throw a flagon of foaming ale into the sea as a sacrifice to that Sjonji. Try as they did, the priests could not stop this heathen custom.

"Fiddler's Green? Well, that's the sailor's idea of the hereafter—not the heaven the Christian preachers speak of, with golden streets and hymns and golden harps. No, a more human heaven, with gay fiddling one could dance a jig or a hornpipe to, and all the things the poor sailor often lacks on his long voyages—steaming, savory food, an abundance of tobacco, and bowls never empty of comforting hot grog."

"Do you believe in Fiddler's Green, sir?"

"I'd not say. It has no concern with me, but I dare say it's been a comforting thought to many a seaman when he faced death upon the waters. I hear bells—your watch? Yes, tomorrow night, same hour—if it's calm, so I can comfortably swim alongside."

THIRD NIGHT

"Well, young man, what do you wish to ask me tonight? What I've seen? I don't talk about it too much, for I'm still a junior member of the family, you see, and I've seen little compared to my elders. My grandfather truly waxes old; he is not quite sure what he actually saw and what he heard from his grandsires. He thinks he saw Ulysses with his fleet of long black galleys landing at Troytown, heard the thunder of that battle, and saw the incredible stratagem of the great Wooden Horse. But this I doubt.

"But my father did see the courageous Columbus leave the port of Palos for that venture upon the Sea of Darkness, and he said, despite all the speeches and the music going and the brave, gay, fluttering flags upon the vessels, it was a sad, a tragic sight. For the women wept upon the quays, not sure if they would ever see their menfolk again.

"As for me—well, I did see the great battle of the Armada, and those overladen Spanish ships, when they went down, were so filled with fine liquors there was not a fish in the Channel or the North Sea could steer a straight course for a week.

"And I saw the Englishmen land at Jamestown, Virginia, in the beautiful treacherous spring, and the Pilgrims go ashore at Plymouth to face the biting teeth of the New England winter. Both times I felt real pity for them in their ignorance.

"I doubt if I see you tomorrow—a storm is coming. The sky was very red this morning—'sailor's warning,' you know—and this afternoon there were signs of wind in the clouds.

> "Mackerel skies and mares' tails
> Make lofty ships carry low sails.

"Trite old sayings, but proved throughout the ages. But I will see you again. Good night, young man."

Captain Barry removed his spectacles and mopped his brow.

"Well, Jerry?"

"I dunno, Captain. Too much readin', I'd say. Plain daft. Maybe he's gone for a fortnight's visit to Atlantis."

"Let us hope, in preference, to Fiddler's Green," said Captain Barry.

There was a knock on the cabin door, and the cook and two cabin boys appeared.

"I am sorry, Captain," the cook said, "but, in spite of my care, there's quite a bit of rum gone. And the boys here have been cleaning up Mr. Smith's cabin. They found ten empty jugs under his bunk."